The Era of Early Civilizations and Empires

Kathy Sammis

WALCH PUBLISHING

User's Guide
to
Walch Reproducible Books

Purchasers of this book are granted the right to reproduce all pages where this symbol appears.

This permission is limited to a single teacher, for classroom use only.

Any questions regarding this policy or requests to purchase further reproduction rights should be addressed to:

Permissions Editor
J. Weston Walch, Publisher
P.O. Box 658
Portland, Maine 04104-0658

1   2   3   4   5   6   7   8   9   10
ISBN 0-8251-4367-5

Copyright © 2002
J. Weston Walch, Publisher
P.O. Box 658 • Portland, Maine 04104-0658
www.walch.com

Printed in the United States of America

CONTENTS

UNIT 3. THE FIRST CIVILIZATIONS

UNIT 4. CIVILIZATIONS SPREAD AND CHANGE

UNIT 5. GREEKS AND PERSIANS

UNIT 6. MAJOR RELIGIONS AND ETHICAL SYSTEMS

UNIT 7. GREAT EMPIRES

TO THE TEACHER

This book covers a wide range of human history, from the emergence of human beings millions of years ago in Africa to the rise and fall of mighty empires in the last centuries B.C.E. and the first centuries C.E. We begin with a look at the development of early humans and their peopling of the globe. Next comes the agricultural revolution, when people transformed their way of life and became settled village dwellers. Villages became towns, towns became cities, and human societies became increasingly complex, leading to the formation of the first civilizations in four river floodplains in Africa and Asia. Soon more civilizations developed, and human interactions around the world increased while cultures diffused and enriched each other. Great empires and major religions appeared; most of the empires crumbled, but the religions endured, and the stamp of ancient cultures endures around the world today.

The activities in this book draw students into the era of early civilizations and empires, so they develop a rich understanding of the variety and significance of ancient world cultures and events. Many activities in this book draw on original source materials, which personalizes distant events and helps students enter into the lives and cultures of ancient times.

The student activity topics are divided into units guided by the National Standards for History (see the Correlation Chart below). Each unit begins with Student Background pages that give the most relevant information on that unit's topic. A number of student activities follow that build skills in decision making, comprehension, analysis, comparing, contrasting, sequencing, interpreting, research, mapping, and role playing.

Each unit includes some Extra Challenge activities to provide enrichment for more advanced or adventurous students. Several maps are provided; you can make copies as needed for applicable activities.

Each unit is preceded by a Teacher's Guide, giving you an overview of the unit and its objectives, plus specific teaching information.

Lower-level students may have some difficulty reading certain primary-source documents that contain some higher-level words and syntax. You might want to review these documents as needed in class.

At the back of this book, you'll find Answers, Additional Activities, and Assessments. You'll also find additional teaching suggestions here. The resource section gives titles of fiction and nonfiction books that will enrich students' learning, plus media/computer research and enrichment resources. The glossary is reproducible for students' use.

Unit	Standards
Unit 1	Era 1, Standards 1A, 1B
Unit 2	Era 1, Standards 2A, 2B; Era 2, Standard 4
Unit 3	Era 2, Standards 1A, 1B, 2A, 4
Unit 4	Era 2, Standards 2B, 3A, 3B, 3C, 3D, 4; Era 3, Standards 1A, 1B, 1C, 1D, 5
Unit 5	Era 3, Standards 2A, 2B, 2C, 2D, 5
Unit 6	Era 3, Standards 1B, 3B, 3C, 3D, 5
Unit 7	Era 3, Standards 3A, 3C, 3D, 5

TO THE STUDENT

Our study of history begins millions of years ago, when human beings first emerged in Africa. Human features developed in a series of changing species. Modern human beings appeared around 35,000 to 40,000 years ago.

As humans developed, they learned to make and use tools. They also learned to speak. They began to work together in simple hunting and gathering bands. Later, these early humans spread out from Africa and peopled the entire globe. Then people learned to become farmers. They grew crops and raised domestic animals. This development process took place over a period of thousands of years.

This agricultural revolution changed human life. Populations grew, and people began to live in settled villages. Villages became towns, and towns became cities. Humans' way of life became more complex. People practiced detailed religious rites. They split into social classes. Their jobs began to focus on single, distinct tasks. Over time, some human societies became so complex that we call them **civilizations.**

These early civilizations first emerged in river floodplains in Africa and different parts of Asia. Soon other civilizations developed in many parts of the world. People migrated, invaded, and traded all through the ancient world. As they did this, their cultures met and mixed. From this meeting and mixing came the first

giant **empires.** (An empire is a collection of nations and peoples ruled over by a single, powerful ruler and central government.) Four great empires formed in ancient times. Two of them ruled over a vast region spread out around the Mediterranean Sea. Alexander the Great created the first of these empires. Roman rulers created the second one. Other great empires took shape in China and in India. By 300 C.E. ("of the common era"), only the Chinese empire remained in existence.

During the era of empire-forming, some of the world's major religions and systems of ethical belief emerged. These included Judaism, Christianity, Hinduism, Buddhism, Confucianism, and Daoism. They spread among people of many different ethnic and political groups. They have had an enduring impact on human history.

The activities you'll do for this course of study will help you better understand this era of early civilizations and great empires. You'll work with maps. You'll put yourself into the shoes of this era's people, describing your life as a slave, taking part in a great battle, planning your across-Asia trading trip. You'll read what this era's people said about themselves and others. You'll read some of the laws they created to rule themselves. When you're done, you'll have a better grasp of these first years of human history.

Name _____ Date _____

Map of the World

Focus on World History:
The Era of Early Civilizations and Empires

Name _____   Date _____

Map of the Ancient World

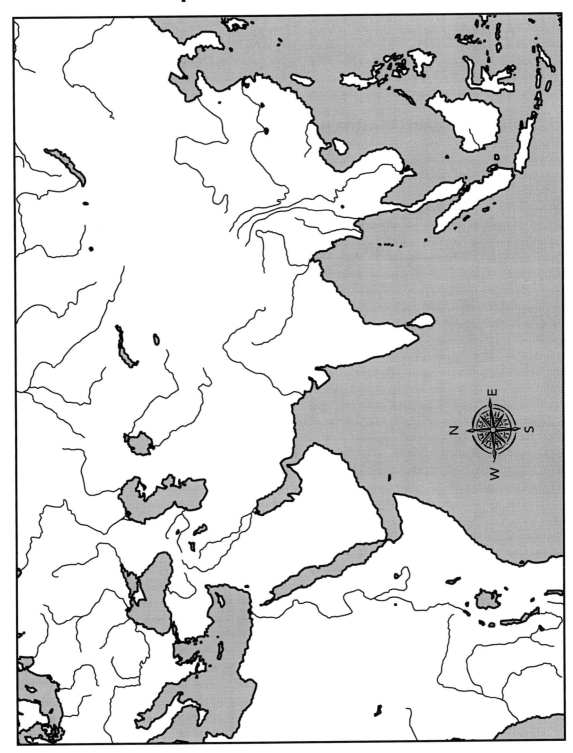

xi   *Focus on World History:*
The Era of Early Civilizations and Empires

Map of Greece and Surrounding Region

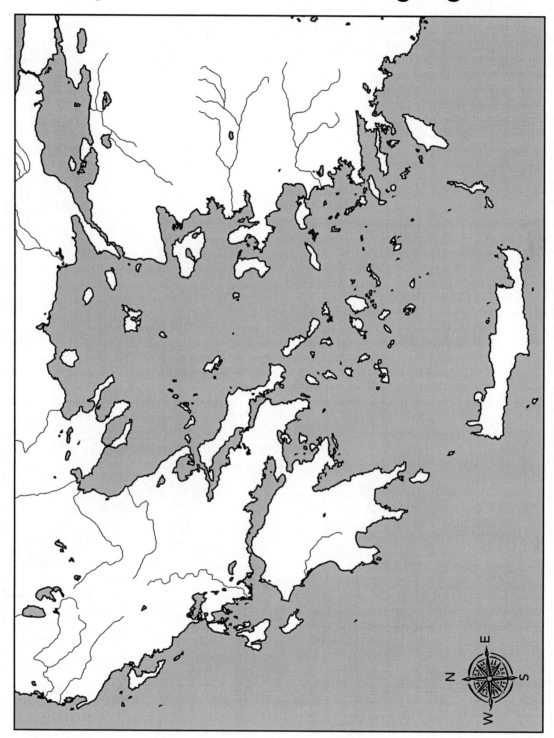

Early Humans

The objectives of this unit are to help students understand what is currently known about the origins of human life, to examine the spread of human beings around the world, and to review the development of very early human societies. As far as we know today, human beings first emerged in Africa and developed in a series of ever-more-capable species until the emergence of *Homo sapiens sapiens,* the modern human being, in about 35,000 B.C.E. About seven hundred thousand to one million years ago, humans began to spread out of Africa.

The human ability to adapt to and manipulate all kinds of contrasting and changing environments allowed humans eventually to inhabit every corner of the globe. Along the way, they learned to make and use various types of tools, they learned to speak, and they learned how to start and use fire. They formed kinship bands, produced paintings, and buried their dead. This primitive life of hunting and gathering lasted for millions of years, from the earliest human species to the end of the last Ice Age. This unit's activities are designed to draw students into a better understanding of these early beginnings of human-kind and of how scientists learn about the facts of prehistory.

Student Activities

Human Beings Emerge presents the various types of hominids, from prehuman to *Homo sapiens sapiens.* Students identify the approximate date and place each type emerged, its main characteristics, and the ways in which it was better adapted for survival than the species that preceded it.

Human Beings Spread Across the World uses mapping to familiarize students with basic geographic features of the world that relate to human migration and also with locations where early human/hominid remains have been found. The worksheet also helps to reinforce students' knowledge of world geography.

Stone Age Tools uses pictures and questions to draw students into identification and understanding of types of Stone Age tools and of the process and significance of developing increasingly sophisticated tools.

Elements of Stone Age Life has students put themselves into the place of a Stone Age human being, describing given aspects of their daily life. Completed worksheets provide a valuable comparison exercise if you assign various students to describe hunter-gatherer communities in different locations around the world, as suggested in the Answer section.

Ötzi the Ice Man uses the remarkable discovery of a mummified Stone Age body in the Italian Alps to show students what kinds of information about early life we discover from archaeological and paleoanthropological finds. The Extra Challenge asks students to construct a biography of Ötzi or write a narrative about the last days of his life.

Discoverers of Prehistory has students identify the type of work done by four specialized fields of science concerned with finding evidence about prehistory. The Extra Challenge asks students to write a job description for one of these careers that they might be interested in pursuing.

Ongoing Discoveries presents summaries of three intriguing recent discoveries. One questions long-held ideas about when and where human beings first learned to use fire. Another yields possible evidence of migration of South Pacific people to the Americas before the arrival of Asian people across the Bering land bridge. The third reports on the discovery of a fossil skull that may challenge "Lucy" as the direct ancestor of modern humans. Directions for you in the Answer section will help you in getting students to begin an ongoing watch for other new discoveries in media of various kinds.

Early Humans

c. 3.5 million B.C.E. to 8000 B.C.E.

Hominid and Human Development

In 1974, Dr. Donald Johanson made a remarkable discovery in eastern Africa. He found a largely complete skeleton of a human-like creature. This young female had lived about 3.5 million years ago. Dr. Johanson and his coworkers nicknamed her Lucy. She was a **hominid** (member of the human family) of the type *Australopithecus afarensis* (African southern ape). Lucy and others of her kind were probably the earliest ancestors of human beings. They walked upright but were quite short. Their brains were the size of apes' brains. *Australopithecus afarensis* occupied many parts of Africa 3 to 4 million years ago.

Between 2 and 3 million years ago, a new **species** and genus emerged. It is called *Homo habilis*, or "skillful human." Its brain was 50 percent larger than the brain of australopithecines. *Homo habilis* had enough brain power to use stones as simple tools and to eat a more varied diet.

> Where did Lucy get her name? Back at camp, Dr. Johanson and his coworkers were playing a tape of the Beatles' song "Lucy in the Sky with Diamonds." Lucy has an Ethiopian name too: Dinquinesh, "thou art wonderful."

Another new species emerged in eastern Africa about 1.6 million years ago. It is called *Homo erectus*, or "upright human." The brain of *Homo erectus* was 30 percent larger than the brain of *Homo habilis*. *Homo erectus* used this greater brain power to learn many new skills. It found out how to control and use fire. It began to hunt large game animals. It learned to make and use hand axes and chopping tools. The body of *Homo erectus* was like a short, stocky version of today's people. The face, however, had a low, sloping forehead, heavy brow ridges, and a receding chin. By about one million years ago, australopithecines and *Homo habilis* no longer existed.

Next came *Homo sapiens* ("wise human"), sometime between 100,000 and 400,000 years ago. The brain of *Homo sapiens* was 30 percent larger than the brain of *Homo erectus*. *Homo sapiens* could speak. It used more sophisticated tools. A subtype was *Homo sapiens neanderthalensis*, the familiar "Neanderthal human." Its head had the apelike features of *Homo erectus*.

Finally came the modern human species, *Homo sapiens sapiens*. These people emerged around 35,000 to 40,000 years ago. The people of today are *Homo sapiens sapiens*.

Hominids
Homo sapiens sapiens 35,000–40,000 years ago
Homo sapiens 100,000–400,000 years ago
Homo erectus 1.6 million years ago
Homo habilis 2–3 million years ago
Australopithecus afarensis 3–4 million years ago

(continued)

Focus on World History:
The Era of Early Civilizations and Empires

Early Humans (continued)

Human Movement Across the Globe

Human beings developed in Africa and stayed there for millions of years. Sometime after about a million years ago, *Homo erectus* began to spread to lands outside of Africa. These people settled widely across Asia and Europe between around 300,000 and 700,000 years ago. *Homo sapiens* and *Homo sapiens sapiens* also probably first appeared in Africa and then spread outward. *Homo sapiens sapiens* displaced Neanderthals in Europe around 30,000 years ago. They also moved into Australia and New Guinea. They took advantage of land bridges (where there is sea today) to **migrate** into Japan and into the Americas from northeastern Asia.

Wherever these early humans went, they were able to adapt to the environment they found. This is a key reason why the species *Homo* came to dominate the globe. People were able to use their mental powers to figure out ways to survive, no matter what conditions they lived in.

Great Rift Valley, Kenya.
Area where many hominid remains
have been found.

Early Human Culture

Prehistoric human beings lived up through the last cold period of the **Ice Age,** which ended about 10,000 years ago. They didn't leave any written records, because writing hadn't been invented yet. But they left many tools. They would have made their tools out of a variety of materials, but most of those that survive are made of stone. Because of this, these years of prehistory are often called the **Stone Age.** Other evidence about Stone Age life comes from rock paintings, pottery, burial sites, animal bones, and carvings.

(continued)

Early Humans *(continued)*

Early human groups were made up of small bands of people. These bands would include several sets of two-parent families, plus children and older and unmated people. Their main task was gathering wild foods to eat. They also hunted wild animals for meat to add to their plant diet. They banded together for protection, for help in caring for children, and to help each other secure enough food to survive. They were **nomadic**—they moved around a lot, following the patterns of ripening plants and migrating animals. They sheltered in huts made of available materials, in dry river beds, under rock overhangings, in caves. People who lived near rivers, lakes, or seas often stayed right there. They didn't need to move around because food was abundant in those waters year-round.

Early humans made many tools. At first, the tools were simple. Then they became more and more complex and useful. *Homo habilis,* for instance, made sharp tools by chipping flakes off hard rocks. *Homo erectus* made and used all-purpose hand axes. *Homo sapiens* made special tools for particular uses, like saws, chisels, and needles. They recorded their way of life in vivid drawings and paintings on the rock walls of their homes. They also buried their dead in graves to which they added pottery, food, and tools—even flowers. Adding items to a grave suggests a belief in an afterlife, a belief that the dead person will need these things in another world.

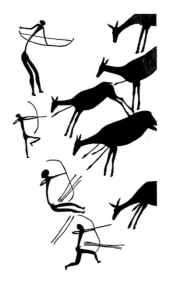

This hunting-and-gathering Stone Age way of life lasted for millions of years. When people began growing their own food and herding their own animals, the Stone Age gave way to the agricultural age. That, in its turn, led to the first civilizations. You'll learn about those changes in Units 2 and 3.

Human Beings Emerge

Directions: Listed below are the various types of hominids, from prehuman to the species that is the modern human. For each, give the approximate date and place the species emerged, its main characteristics, and the main way(s) in which it was better adapted for survival than the species that came before it.

1. *Australopithecus afarensis* (African southern ape)
   Date, place: _____
   Characteristics, adaptations: _____
   _____
   _____

2. *Homo habilis* ("skillful human")
   Date, place: _____
   Characteristics, adaptations: _____
   _____
   _____

3. *Homo erectus* ("upright human")
   Date, place: _____
   Characteristics, adaptations: _____
   _____
   _____

4. *Homo sapiens* ("wise human")
   Date, place: _____
   Characteristics, adaptations: _____
   _____
   _____

5. *Homo sapiens sapiens* ("wise wise human")
   Date, place: _____
   Characteristics, adaptations: _____
   _____
   _____

Human Beings Spread Across the World

Part 1 Directions: On your map of the world, do the following:

1. Label the continents.
2. Draw in land bridges with colored pencils.
3. Show geographical barriers to migrations (major deserts, mountains, oceans/seas).
4. Show with arrows the spread (plus approximate dates) of humans out of Africa and around the world.

Part 2 Directions: Locate and label on your map these sites where early human/hominid remains have been found.

Lake Turkana, Kenya (*Homo erectus*)

Hadar, Ethiopia (Lucy, *Australopithecus afarensis*)

Laetoli, Tanzania (various hominids)

Olduvai Gorge, Tanzania (*Homo habilis* and *Homo erectus*)

Great Rift Valley, Kenya (various hominids)

Sterkfontein, South Africa (*Australopithecus afarensis*)

Neander Valley, Germany (Neanderthals)

Shanidar cave, Iran (Neanderthals)

Zhoukoudian cave, China (*Homo erectus,* possible controlled use of fire)

Vértesszöllös, Hungary (*Homo erectus,* campfire)

Java ("Java man," *Homo erectus*)

Swanscombe, Britain (*Homo erectus*)

Belo Horizonte, Brazil (just north of Rio de Janeiro) (early skull, possibly from Polynesia)

Altamira, Spain (rock/cave paintings)

Lascaux, France (rock/cave paintings)

Folsom or Clovis, southwest North America (early tools, *Homo sapiens*)

Monte Verde, Fell's Cave, South America (early tools, *Homo sapiens*)

Ternifine, northwest Africa (*Homo erectus*)

Mapa, Southeast Asia (*Homo sapiens*)

Stone Age Tools

Directions: Look closely at the illustration below. It shows Germanic men of the Stone Age. List the various tools you see in the picture. Then decide which type of hominid or human these men most likely are. Support your answers with evidence from the picture.

Tools shown: _____

_____

_____

Hominid or human type: _____

Evidence: _____

_____

_____

Elements of Stone Age Life

Directions: Put yourself in the place of a human living in the Stone Age. Describe the aspects of your daily life that are listed below. Remember, people lived in many different places and kinds of climates and societies during the Stone Age.

1. Where in the world (geographically) you live: _____

    _____

2. Specific site(s) where you live and your type of dwelling place(s): _____

    _____

    _____

3. Size of your band and its makeup (who, how many): _____

    _____

    _____

4. Your family structure: _____

    _____

    _____

5. Your diet (what you eat and how you get these items): _____

    _____

    _____

6. Tools you use in daily life: _____

    _____

    _____

7. Your clothing: _____

    _____

    _____

8. Your knowledge of your natural environment: _____

    _____

    _____

9. Effects your band may be having on your natural environment: _____

    _____

    _____

10. Your artistic expression: _____

    _____

    _____

11. Your religious beliefs: _____

    _____

    _____

Ötzi the Ice Man

Directions: Two German hikers made a remarkable find in the Ötzaler Alps of Italy in 1991. They came across the mummified body of a man who had died there 5,000 years ago. The clothing and equipment of Ötzi the Ice Man told researchers a lot about this Stone Age man and his life and the life of his people. Do some research and fill in the information about Ötzi the Ice Man in the categories below. What things of each type was Ötzi wearing or carrying with him?

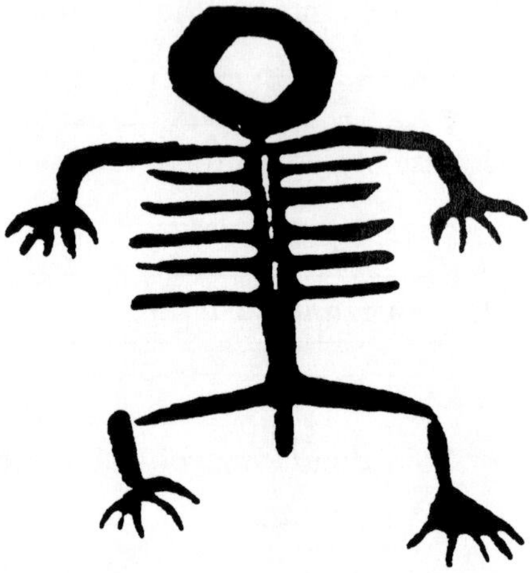

1. clothing: _____

   _____

   _____

   _____

2. hunting items: _____

   _____

   _____

3. tools: _____

   _____

   _____

   _____

4. medical supplies: _____

   _____

   _____

   _____

5. containers: _____

   _____

   _____

Extra Challenge: Construct a biography of Ötzi or a narrative about the last week of his life. Include illustrations of Ötzi and the items found with him.

Discoverers of Prehistory

Directions: How do we find out about life before recorded human history? Scientists who specialize in specific areas of knowledge search for evidence. Among them are geologists, archaeologists, paleontologists, and paleoanthropologists. What type of prehistoric evidence does each of these types of scientists search for and interpret? Answer this question in the spaces below.

1. geologist: _____
   _____
   _____
   _____
   _____

2. archaeologist: _____
   _____
   _____
   _____
   _____

3. paleontologist: _____
   _____
   _____
   _____
   _____

4. paleoanthropologist: _____
   _____
   _____
   _____
   _____

Extra Challenge: Which of the careers above might interest you? Write a job description for that career. Include required training and interests, and possible areas of investigation that the job might cover.

Ongoing Discoveries

Archaeologists and paleoanthropologists are not desk-bound scientists. They don't just study remains that have already been found. They go out in the field and make new discoveries. Sometimes those new discoveries rewrite what we think we know about the origins of human beings. Here are three examples, summaries of news stories.

May 1998: "Ancient Skull in Brazil Puts New Light on Migration"

Researchers found an 11,500-year-old skull in Belo Horizonte, about 200 miles north of Rio de Janeiro, in Brazil. It is probably the skull of a young woman aged 20 to 25. Her finders called her Luzia, the Portuguese name for Lucy. [You read about Lucy on the Student Background pages for this unit.] This is the oldest skull found in the Americas so far. Anthropologists say Luzia came from the South Pacific. She is not one of the Mongoloid people who crossed the land bridge from northeast Asia into the Americas during the Ice Age. Her skull and teeth are like those of the people who live in the South Pacific today. At 11,500 years old, Luzia's remains are older than the presumed date of the Bering migration, 10,000 to 11,000 years ago. This means that South Pacificans may have reached the Americas, especially South America, before the Northeast Asians did.

July 1998: "New Evidence Disputes Fire-Discovery Theories"

Zhoukoudian cave, near Beijing, in China, has long been thought to contain the remains of the earliest known campfire. Scientists had found burned animal bones in the cave. They thought that was evidence of deliberate human use of fire by *Homo erectus* nearly 500,000 years ago. However, a new analysis of the cave soils showed no evidence of wood ash or other signs of fire being used there. So the cave may never have been a human home, even though many textbooks say it was. The next best evidence of human mastery of fire is in a camp near Vértesszöllös, Hungary, 200,000 to 400,000 years ago. This is important, because *Homo erectus* couldn't have moved into colder regions from Africa until they had the use of fire.

March 2001: "Ancient Skull May Be New Human Link"

Anthropologists have discovered an unusual 3.5-million-year-old skull in Kenya. Its finders have named the creature *Kenyanthropus platyops*, or "Kenyan Flat-face." As a new genus, this fossil is in a different lineage from Lucy. Thus, scientists suggest that either *kenyanthropus* or *australopithecus*—but not both of them—could be the direct ancestor of modern humans.

The Agricultural Revolution

The objective of this unit is to help students understand the agricultural revolution—the vital change from hunting and gathering to the agricultural way of life that began about 10,000 years ago. Over a period of several thousand years, people learned to domesticate plants and animals, producing their own food by growing crops and raising domestic animals. This change seems to have occurred independently in many areas of the world, and it had an enormous impact on human life. People began to live in settled villages, population increased, and society became more complex, with new features such as division of labor, trade, and elaborate religious shrines. This unit's activities are designed to draw students into a better understanding of the process and significance of this agricultural revolution.

Student Activities

Animals and Crops Around the World uses a matching exercise to help students realize that different animals and crops are well adapted to different regions of the world. The Extra Challenge extends the activity through mapping, so students can see the worldwide distribution of agricultural societies and the diversity of animals and crops.

Agricultural Tools asks students to explain the use of various early farming tools. By doing so, they gain an understanding of how changes in human activities can create a need for new technology. The Extra Challenge asks students to create a class exhibit of Neolithic farming tools.

Farming Techniques helps students understand how different local conditions require people to develop different ways to grow crops. Students describe five given ways of acquiring and using needed water in five different geographic areas. The Extra Challenge asks students to draw a diagram or create a model of one of these water-use techniques.

Why Be a Farmer? puts students in the place of a member of an early farming community, responding to a hunter-gatherer's observations about the very real disadvantages of the farming way of life. Role-play allows students then to respond, explaining the (also) very real advantages of the farming way of life.

Specializing uses a flow chart to illustrate the process of specialization, using as an example moving from being a herder who tends, slaughters, and processes all of a group's domestic animals through various steps to the specialized trades of clothes maker and blanket maker. Students create a similar specialization flow chart for some other early agricultural occupation.

The Evidence of Archaeology has students become archaeologists by identifying which type of society would leave behind specific, listed types of remains.

Climate and Lifestyle draws students into an understanding of how climate and environment affect a people's way of life by asking them a series of questions about why they would choose one specific way of life over another specific one in a particular area of the world.

A Neolithic Village provides a framework for students to fill in with facts about a specific prehistoric agricultural village site that they choose to investigate, from a list of sites given. The Extra Challenge invites students to create an illustration, diorama, or photographic image display of their chosen village.

The Agricultural Revolution

c. 10,000 B.C.E. to 4000 B.C.E.

Around 10,000 years ago, human beings began a profound change in their way of life. For millions of years, they had hunted and gathered their food from wild animals and plants. Now they began to grow their own food plants and keep herds of domestic animals.

This period is often called the "Neolithic revolution." **Neolithic** means "New Stone Age." The term recognizes the new types of stone tools that people began making in the later years of the Stone Age. But scientists now know it was not new tools that marked the deep changes in human life during this era. The truly important change was the shift to food production. We call this shift the **agricultural revolution.**

We don't know just how or when or where people first learned to become farmers. Women gathered much of the wild plant foods. Most likely, they began to notice that a certain plant grew in a place where they had spilled seeds of that plant. Wandering bands of hunter-gatherers often came back to favorite camps at certain seasons of the year. They probably began to sow seeds there of plants they favored. Then the plants would be growing there the next time they returned to the camp.

A change in the climate 10,000 years ago would have encouraged this new approach to food production. The last Ice Age ended then. The world became generally warmer. This made many areas more favorable for growing food crops.

The switch from wild-food gathering to food production had a huge impact on human life. People began to live in settled villages. They no longer had to roam from place to place to find their food. Their food plants and animals were right at hand, all the time. People learned which crops grew best for their climate. For example:

- Middle East—wheat and barley
- tropical Africa—root crops
- Southeast Asia—rice
- northern China—millet

As people gained experience in farming, they developed special tools and techniques to help them. Examples include sickle blades and the plow.

Earlier people had **domesticated** dogs and goats. Agricultural people domesticated many more animals. They also bred new species of animals. For example:

- Middle East—sheep
- Africa—cattle
- India and China—water buffalo and pigs
- the Americas—llamas

Domestic animals provided people with milk, hides, meat, and wool. They also provided muscle power, pulling carts and plows to help with the farming. Animals were vital in dry areas not suitable for farming, like the Sahara and central Asia. There, people became **pastoralists.** That is, they developed a way of life that revolved around their large herds of animals.

(continued)

The Agricultural Revolution *(continued)*

With the food supply more secure and abundant, populations increased. Villages formed, and some grew into towns. Not everyone had to spend all their time producing food. In their spare time, people made pottery, wove cloth and baskets, and created objects with metals. Some people even worked full-time at making crafts. Others became religious leaders. Beliefs most often centered on a female Earth Mother and a male Sky God. Townspeople banded together to build village structures. They often created village religious shrines. They built places to store the village's food supply. People also developed rules to make town life orderly. All these steps formed the solid base from which the first civilizations would emerge.

Farming as a way of life seems to have developed on its own in many different areas of the world over the course of thousands of years. However, not all people everywhere became farmers. Many people continued their nomadic hunter-gatherer ways of life. This was especially true in dry climates not suited for farming. Other people lived in settled fishing villages, herded reindeer, hunted bison. Yet the agricultural societies pointed the way to the future.

Animals and Crops Around the World

Directions: Listed below are plants and animals that were grown and tended by early farming peoples. For each, name the region or regions where each crop or animal was an important feature of that region's agriculture and/or herding. Regions to choose from are:

Central/South America   Europe   Southeast Asia
North America   Middle East   China
sub-Saharan Africa   North Africa   India

Animals	**Plants**
sheep _____	wheat _____
goat _____	barley _____
cattle _____	millet _____
pig _____	lentil _____
guinea pig _____	rice _____
water buffalo _____	maize _____
llama _____	sorghum _____
reindeer _____	yam _____
turkey _____	banana _____
chicken _____	potato _____
	sunflower _____

Extra Challenge: Locate and label these regions, plants, and animals on your map of the world.

17   *Focus on World History:*
                                                        The Era of Early Civilizations and Empires

Agricultural Tools

Directions: The change from hunting-gathering to agriculture made it necessary for people to invent new tools to help them farm. Named below are some vital tools that were developed during the agricultural revolution. Explain what each one was used for.

1. sickle blade

   Use:_____

   _____

2. wooden plow

   Use:_____

   _____

3. wheeled cart

   Use:_____

   _____

4. axe

   Use:_____

   _____

5. hoe

   Use:_____

   _____

6. grindstone/mortar-pestle

   Use:_____

   _____

7. People learned to make pottery (containers made of hardened clay) during the agricultural revolution. Why would pottery have been a very important "tool" for farming people to have?

   _____

   _____

   _____

8. What changes could people make in their diet once they had pottery?

   _____

   _____

   _____

Extra Challenge: Do some research and try to find an image of several of the tools named above. Combine your images with those of classmates to create a class exhibit of Neolithic farming tools.

Farming Techniques

Directions: Water is essential for agriculture. People around the world farmed in many areas where they could not rely on simple, natural rainfall to water their crops. Different people in different parts of the world developed various ways to get the water they needed. Research and describe each farming technique named below. Why was each well adapted for the place where people used it?

1. Egypt—harnessing the floodwaters of the Nile River

   _____

   _____

2. Mesopotamia—using the waters of the Tigris and Euphrates rivers

   _____

   _____

3. Iran—developing an underground water supply

   _____

   _____

4. New Guinea and Mesoamerica—developing the drained-field technique

   _____

   _____

5. Southeast Asia—using wet-rice agriculture

   _____

   _____

Extra Challenge: Draw a diagram or build a model of one of these agricultural techniques.

Why Be a Farmer?

Directions: For this activity, imagine that you are a member of a group that has taken up a farming way of life. You and your fellow group members grow field crops, keep domestic animals, and live in a settled village. One day, a member of a hunting-gathering group visits your village. This person is very curious about your new way of living. She stays and observes everything that goes on in your village for several days. She thinks she sees a lot of disadvantages to the farming way of life. Read her comments below. Then admit in what way each is accurate, if it is. (You will have a chance to defend your way of life after this.)

1. "I think you work a lot harder and longer than I do to get the food you need." _____

   _____

   _____

2. "I think my diet is better than yours." _____

   _____

   _____

3. "I think your village is an unhealthy place to live." _____

   _____

   _____

4. "I think my way of life is more secure than yours." _____

   _____

   _____

5. "I think the farming way of life will lead to more conflicts between groups of people."

   _____

   _____

6. "Don't you have to put in a lot of extra work to build all those walls and public buildings in your village?"

   _____

   _____

Now role-play a discussion between you and your visitor in which you explain the advantages of the farming way of life.

                                       Focus on World History:
                                                                            The Era of Early Civilizations and Empires

Specializing

Once people settled in villages and began producing surplus food, the labor of the group began to divide. In hunter-gatherer societies, every group member took part in almost all the tasks of life. In villages, people began to **specialize.** That is, certain people performed only certain tasks. Here's a chart of how one activity became more and more specialized over time.

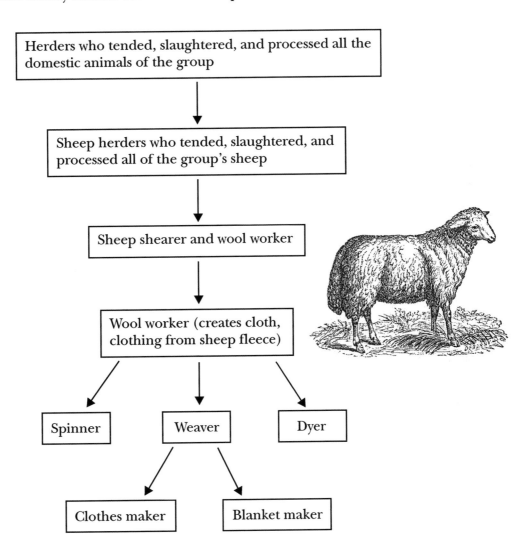

Directions: Create a similar specialization flowchart for some other occupations in early agricultural times. Share charts with classmates.

Focus on World History:
The Era of Early Civilizations and Empires

The Evidence of Archaeology

Directions: Suppose you are an archaeologist studying ancient remains. Listed below are various remains and artifacts you have found at different sites. What type of early society would leave behind each of these remains and artifacts?

1. a skeleton dressed in animal skins

2. very large pottery containers

3. shell midden,* no building remains

4. a plastered-over skull

5. irrigation ditches

6. wild gazelle bones

7. a battle-axe

8. skeleton of an old man with a withered, useless arm

9. a statue of a well-rounded female figure

10. a sickle

11. animal-bone huts

12. bones of goats, mostly young males and much older females

13. a spear and a spear-thrower

14. a number of large hut foundations

15. a sacred grove

*heap of discarded shells from edible shellfish

*Focus on World History:
The Era of Early Civilizations and Empires*

Climate and Lifestyle

Directions: Climate and environment affect a people's way of life. To understand this better, answer the following questions.

Why would you . . .

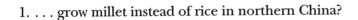

1. . . . grow millet instead of rice in northern China?

2. . . . grow rice instead of millet in southern China?

3. . . . grow root crops instead of wheat in equatorial West Africa?

4. . . . hunt bison instead of grow corn in the grasslands of North America?

5. . . . stay with hunting-gathering instead of farming in Australia?

6. . . . switch from farming to herding in the Sahara?

7. . . . grow local grains instead of Mideast barley in sub-Saharan Africa?

8. . . . take up reindeer herding in northern Eurasia?

9. . . . choose pastoralism over agriculture in central Asia?

10. . . . concentrate on farming rather than herding in Mesoamerica?

A Neolithic Village

Directions: Scientists have uncovered and studied a number of Neolithic village remains around the world. Choose one of those sites listed on the following page to investigate. Use the information you find to fill in as many boxes of this chart as you can.

Years when this village flourished	Geographic location of village	Size of village (area, population)
Natural environment around village	Adaptations to environment	Evidence of natural disaster
Dwellings—types, sizes, building materials	Communal structures	Fortifications
Plant remains	Animal remains	Clothing remains
Tools	Weapons	Evidence of trade
Craft artifacts	Leisure-activity artifacts	Artworks
Burial sites and contents	Evidence of belief system	Evidence of social class differences

(continued)

A Neolithic Village *(continued)*

Directions: To complete the Worksheet 8 chart, investigate one of the following agricultural village sites:

Jarmo (Iraq)	Catal Huyuk (Turkey)	Petra (Jordan)
Banpo (China)	Skara Brae (Scotland)	Tehuacán Valley (Mexico)

Skara Brae

Extra Challenge: Create a mural illustration or a diorama of the prehistoric village you have investigated. Or, create a display of photographic or video images of the village site.

The First Civilizations

The objectives of this unit are to help students understand the nature of civilization, to examine the process by which civilizations emerged and developed, and to explore the specific characteristics of the four early river floodplain civilizations in Mesopotamia, the Nile River valley, the Indus River valley, and the Huang He (Yellow) River valley. Civilizations first emerged in river valleys because of the extremely fertile soil created by periodic flooding. These environments could support a very dense population, and so cities developed. Central governments arose to direct the labor-intensive flood-control and irrigation projects that made farming possible. These complex societies developed more attributes of civilization—division of social classes, complex religions and religious rituals, monumental building, bronze-working and ironworking skills, writing and record-keeping systems, and advanced intellectual and artistic achievements. This unit's activities are designed to draw students into a greater understanding of this process in early civilizations.

Student Activities

Mapping the Early Civilized World uses mapping to familiarize students with the geography of the early civilizations, and to help them recognize barriers and lack of barriers to invasion, trade, and migration in the early civilized regions. The Extra Challenge invites students to compare elements of climate and geography among the four river floodplain regions.

Ancient Monuments shows students pictures of four distinct types of early, huge monuments, one mark of civilization. Students identify the type of each, the civilization that created it, and the purpose of such a monument.

Civilization and Social Classes has students develop hierarchy charts, using a list of specific social classes (another mark of civilization), in early Mesopotamia and early China. The Extra Challenge asks students to put themselves in the place of a person in one of the named social classes in Mesopotamia or China and describe his or her daily life.

Building the Pyramids uses Egyptian inscriptions and the report of an ancient Greek historian to describe aspects of the human effort involved in building the pyramids. Students put themselves in the place of a person called into forced labor to help build a pyramid and write journal entries or role-play a conversation about their experience.

The Need for Technology presents important technological advances (another mark of civilization) and has students explain what forces in specific societies pushed each civilization to develop the named technology. This reinforces the concept that technology arises in response to particular human needs. The Extra Challenge asks students which later civilizations and peoples developed two additional technologies.

Origins of Writing presents another mark of civilization, the development of writing systems. Students identify which of three types of writing are shown, which civilization developed each type, and for what purpose each civilization developed its writing system. The Challenge Question asks students to consider the potential limitations of these early writing systems. The Extra Challenge invites students to investigate the Indus Valley writing system.

The Mighty Gilgamesh presents excerpts from the ancient Mesopotamian epic poem, *The Epic of Gilgamesh*. Questions help students identify the various aspects of Mesopotamian life that each excerpt reveals. The Extra Challenge asks students to read the entire epic to find out how it turns out (and maybe find out why the worksheet says the epic is about fierce battles, larger-than-life heroes, sex, death, and a dangerous journey) and learn yet more about Mesopotamian culture.

Marks of Civilization provides a framework for students to use in identifying specific elements in one early civilization that match listed characteristics applying to most civilizations. A follow-up class discussion allows students to contrast and compare the four early floodplain civilizations.

The First Civilizations

c. 4000 B.C.E. to 2000 B.C.E.

People first began living in settled villages around 6000 B.C.E. Over time, many of these villages grew. Their human societies became more complex. In the floodplains of four great river systems, human culture developed into the advanced, complex stage we call civilization.

River Floodplain Civilizations
Tigris & Euphrates rivers (Mesopotamia/southwest Asia)—c. 4000 B.C.E.
Nile River (Egypt/Africa)—c. 4000 B.C.E.
Indus River (India)—c. 2500 B.C.E.
Huang He (Yellow) River (China)—c. 2000 B.C.E.

Civilizations first developed in river valleys because of the floods there. At least once a year, the great rivers would overrun their banks. These floods left behind silt, which made the soil very fertile. But farming was possible only if large numbers of people worked together. They had to build and maintain large-scale irrigation and flood-control projects. This required a central government to plan and direct the work. As farming produced more food, populations grew. Cities developed and got larger. Many people worked at jobs other than farming. They banded together to build great monuments and temples to honor their **deities.** They built grand structures to house their high government officials.

What makes a society a civilization? Most civilizations would have the following characteristics:

- A complex, well-organized government
- Division of social classes
- Cities and monumental buildings
- Advanced technical skills, such as bronze and iron metalworking
- Division (specialization) of labor
- Writing and record-keeping systems
- A complex religion and religious rituals
- Advanced intellectual and artistic achievements

A brief look at the four great early civilizations will show that they feature the elements in this list.

Mesopotamia

Mesopotamia is the area between and around the Tigris and Euphrates rivers in southwest Asia. (The word *Mesopotamia* means "between rivers.") The first civilization here developed in Sumer, in the lower part of the area. Sumer was a collection of many small **city-states.** (A city-state is a city and the surrounding villages and farmlands it controls.) The city-states often fought over water rights and boundary lines. But they cooperated, too, and traded widely with each other. Both kings and priests wielded power in the cities. Each Sumerian city had a temple devoted to the deity or deities who belonged to that community.

> In which of today's nations is Mesopotamia located?
>
> Iraq

(continued)

The First Civilizations *(continued)*

The Sumerians were very inventive. They developed a wedge-shaped form of writing on clay tablets. This writing system is called **cuneiform.** The people of Sumer built and maintained a widespread system of canals, dams, and dikes. This system harnessed and controlled the river waters. The Sumerians also developed a lunar calendar and a number system based on 60.

> Look at the face of a nondigital watch. The way it is divided into seconds and minutes comes from the base-60 Sumerian number system.

Sumerian society was divided into three classes. The top class was made up of free landowners, including priests and warriors. Next came artisans and farmers attached to lands owned by royalty or the temple. At the bottom were slaves. Most Sumerians were farmers whose work supported the temples and cities and trade.

Sumerian religion reflected the forces of nature in the region. The annual river floods were violent and unpredictable. So were Sumerian gods. Sumerians believed the gods treated human beings as playthings and needed constantly to be appeased.

Egypt

Egypt is located in the northeastern corner of Africa, where Asia and Africa meet. Civilization developed in Egypt in the only place it could: in the narrow green valley of the Nile River, which flows through the country from south to north. On either side of the valley stretch wide deserts. The Nile delta empties into the Mediterranean Sea along Egypt's north border. The delta offers no natural harbors. So Egypt developed its culture quite isolated from other civilizations and peoples.

As in Sumer, farming in Egypt depended on water from river floods. But unlike in Sumer, the annual Nile flood was predictable. It came at the right time for grain growing. Egyptians used dikes and canals to hold and carry the river water as needed. The Nile also provided an excellent route for trade. Egypt had many other natural resources, so it was quite self-sufficient.

(continued)

The First Civilizations (continued)

Unlike Mesopotamia, Egypt became united under one strong king, or pharaoh. This happened early in Egypt's history, around 3000 B.C.E. The pharaoh was considered to be the son of the great sun-god, Re. His task was to rule the land and take care of its people on behalf of the god. The pharaoh strictly controlled all aspects of Egyptian life, including commerce. He and his top officials and priests lived in central cities. The vast majority of Egyptians, however, lived in farming villages.

Social classes in Egypt were not tightly defined. An upper class of nobles, priests, and high-level officials existed. Below them were all the other people, mostly peasant farmers. Women enjoyed more rights and higher status in Egypt than in other civilizations of the time. During later years, the Egyptian empire expanded. Captives then became slaves and formed a lower class.

Religion was very important to Egyptians. They viewed the cosmos as an orderly place. They felt that their gods protected them. They had a deep belief in an afterlife. This led them to build grand tombs for members of the higher classes. Huge pyramids housed dead pharaohs. Concern about the afterlife also led Egyptians to develop highly refined ways to mummify, or preserve, dead bodies.

Egyptians developed a unique form of symbol-based writing called **hieroglyphics.** They also invented a writing material made from reeds called **papyrus.** Egyptians crafted a lunar calendar. They developed a number system based on 10 (like our decimal system). They also learned a great deal about anatomy and medicine.

Indus River valley

The Indus River floodplain lies in what is Pakistan today. An early civilization developed here around 2500 B.C.E. Indus River valley dwellers used the two annual floods of the river to plant and harvest two crops a year. Our knowledge of the Indus Valley civilization is limited. These people had a system of writing, but no one has been able to decipher it. Two major urban centers have been unearthed, Harappa and Mohenjo-Daro. These cities had large buildings, straight streets, and water and sewer systems. Each had a citadel—several large buildings set in a raised and enclosed compound. Artisans in the cities produced fine trade goods such as pottery, jewelry, and bronze sculptures. The Indus River valley cities died out sometime after 1800 B.C.E. The cause might have been hostile invasions or environmental problems.

> The Indus River floods twice a year: once in early spring from melting mountain snows and again in late summer from the monsoon rains.

(continued)

The First Civilizations *(continued)*

Shang China

A fourth river floodplain civilization arose in China around 2000 B.C.E. It was centered along the Huang He, or Yellow, River. Like Egypt, China is separated from other countries by natural barriers—mountains, deserts, and seas. The ancient Chinese did engage in some trade with other cultures. But mostly, as in Egypt, Chinese civilization developed on its own.

The Huang He region is in the northern part of China. Relatively little rain falls here. Farming (mainly of millet) depends on **irrigation** and flood control. Dikes must hold the river back during flood stage. Drainage canals must take away excess flood water. Irrigation canals must bring water in during dry periods. An early people, the Shang, formed a central government to organize and direct these projects. The Shang founded the first recorded Chinese **dynasty** around 1500 B.C.E. (A dynasty is a series of rulers from the same set of families.) The Shang controlled a large area. Their ruler was a hereditary king. A noble class of warriors and high-level officials helped the king rule. The warriors often fought to push back nomadic "barbarians" to the north and west of the kingdom. The rulers oversaw the construction of large cities and massive royal tombs.

The early Chinese developed a unique system of writing. They used a complex set of characters that stood for parts of words, things, and ideas. They also drew up a complex but useful calendar. Artisans and artists were very skilled, especially in pottery and bronze work. (Only upper-class people had bronze objects, though. Peasants continued to use stone tools.) Religion focused on concern for ancestors and on attempts to find out the will of the gods. Ancestors, as well as aged family members, were revered. In life, children had a duty to obey and respect their parents in all things. In death, the Chinese believed their ancestors looked over them and could intervene with the gods on their behalf. The Chinese also saw events in nature as signs of the gods' will. Their priests wrote questions on animal bones, called oracle bones. They then heated the bones and read messages from the gods in the resulting pattern of cracks.

Rice paddies, Xingping, Guangxi (China)

Focus on World History:
The Era of Early Civilizations and Empires

Mapping the Early Civilized World

Directions: Geography very much affected the way river floodplain civilizations developed and interacted. Learn more about this. Locate the following on your map of the ancient world. Then answer the questions that follow.

Rivers (Color in blue)		**Large Bodies of Water** (Color in blue)	
Tigris	Mekong	Mediterranean Sea	Persian Gulf
Euphrates	Yangzi	Red Sea	Indian Ocean
Nile	Huang He	Black Sea	Bay of Bengal
Ganges	(Yellow)	Caspian Sea	Yellow Sea
Indus		Arabian Sea	Pacific Ocean

Mountains (Color in gray)	**Deserts** (Color in tan)	**Civilization/Settlement Areas** (Color in green)	
Zagros	Arabian	Mesopotamia	India
Caucasus	Sahara	Egypt	China
Himalaya	Gobi	Arabia	Southeast Asia
Hindu Kush	Thar		

Cities	
Sumer	Harappa
Anyang	Mohenjo-Daro
Memphis	

Now study your completed map and answer these questions.

1. What barriers do you see that would tend to keep any of these river floodplain civilizations fairly isolated and secure from invasions? _____

_____

2. What features do you see that would make trade, migration, and invasion possible—even easy—for any of these civilizations? _____

_____

Extra Challenge: Create a chart that compares features of the climate and geography of the Huang He, Indus River, Mesopotamia, and Nile River regions.

Ancient Monuments

Directions: Different ancient civilizations created various types of huge monuments for varying reasons. For each monument shown below, tell what type of monument it is, which civilization built such monuments, and what the purpose of such a monument was.

1.

Type: _____

Civilization: _____

Purpose: _____

_____

3.

Type: _____

Civilization: _____

Purpose: _____

_____

2.

Type: _____

Civilization: _____

Purpose: _____

_____

4.

Type: _____

Civilization: _____

Purpose: _____

_____

Extra Challenge: Construct a model of one of these types of monuments.

Civilization and Social Classes

Directions: When human societies developed into civilizations, social classes developed. Certain classes had a higher status than others. Some classes were more or less equal. Sort the classes named below into a hierarchy chart. Show the most powerful class(es) in box(es) at the top, the next most powerful below them, and so on. Draw lines to connect boxes at each level with boxes directly above them. Create one hierarchy chart for a typical ancient Mesopotamian culture and another for the ancient Chinese. You can draw one of your hierarchy charts in the space below. When your charts are complete, decide where women fit in. What were the roles and status of women in these societies?

warriors	shopkeepers	local leaders/rulers
slaves	government officials	artisans
priests/shamans	merchants	nobility/elite families
scribes	king/ruler	farmers/peasants

Extra Challenge: Become an ancient Mesopotamian or Chinese person. Put yourself in the place of a person (woman, man, or child) in one of the classes listed above and describe your daily life.

Building the Pyramids

We have very little in the way of on-the-spot narratives describing the incredible human effort expended in building Egypt's mammoth pyramids. But we do have the report of Herodotus, a Greek historian. He visited Egypt in about 460 B.C.E. From information he gathered during that visit, Herodotus described the building of the Great Pyramid of Cheops (Khufu) 2,000 years earlier.

Cheops closed the temples, and forbid the Egyptians to offer sacrifice, forcing them instead to labor, one and all, in his service. Some were required to drag blocks of stone down to the Nile from the quarries in the Arabian range of hills. Others received the blocks after they had been ferried in boats across the river, and dragged them to the Libyan range of hills. A hundred thousand men labored constantly, and were relieved every three months by a fresh lot.

It took ten years' oppression of the people to make the causeway for the conveyance of the stones, a work not much less than building the pyramid itself. This causeway is 3,000 feet long and 60 feet wide and 50 feet in height at the highest part. It is built of polished stone and is covered with carvings of animals. To make it took ten years, as I said—or rather to make the causeway, the works on the mound where the pyramid stands, and the underground chambers. Cheops intended the chambers as vaults for his own use: these last were built on a sort of island, surrounded by water introduced from the Nile by a canal.

The pyramid itself was twenty years in building. It is a square, eight hundred feet each way, and the height the same, built entirely of polished stone, fitted together with the utmost care. The stones of which it is composed are none of them less than thirty feet in length.

The pyramid was built in steps. . . . After laying the stones for the base, the workmen raised the remaining stones to their places with levers formed of short wooden planks. The first lever raised the block from the ground to the top of the first step. On this step was another lever, which received the block and carried it to the second step [and so on]. . . .

There is an inscription in Egyptian characters on the pyramid which records the quantity of radishes, onions, and garlic that the workmen ate.

An inscription in an Egyptian king's tomb describes the difficulties of transporting huge blocks of stone for the Egyptian kings' statues and pyramids.

Tomb of Thuthotep, c. 1850 B.C.E.

A statue of 13 cubits [about 20 feet tall] [was brought]. The roadway, upon which it came, was very difficult, beyond anything. The dragging of the great statue upon it was hard for the heart of the people, because of the difficult, hard stone on the ground.

(continued)

Building the Pyramids *(continued)*

What kept the men at work? A tomb picture shows an overseer watching his crew of workers. The inscription includes this comment:

Temple of Amon, c. 1460 B.C.E.

The workmen say, "The taskmaster gives us bread, beer, and every good thing; he leads us, with a loving heart for the king, Thutmose III, who builds the temple of the gods." The taskmaster says to the builders: "The rod is in my hand; be not idle."

Ineni was superintendent of building projects for pharaoh Thutmose I. He described a boat built to transport two huge stone obelisks. (An obelisk is a tapering, four-sided stone shaft.)

Hall of Karnak, c. 1460 B.C.E.

I oversaw the erection of two obelisks. I watched over the building of a splendid boat, 120 cubits long [about 200 feet], 40 cubits wide [about 65 feet], to transport these obelisks. They arrived safely in good condition at Karnak.

Temple of Karnak

Directions: Imagine you are one of the people called into forced labor to help build a pyramid. Write a series of journal entries about your experience, based on these inscriptions and what you know about ancient Egyptian life. Or, role-play a conversation among workers after a long day's work. Do you work willingly, or are you resentful? Do you worry about your family back home? Are you fed well and treated well?

                                       Focus on World History:
The Era of Early Civilizations and Empires

The Need for Technology

Directions: Technology develops and advances because of people's needs—to build, to grow crops, to make war, understand the world. People in ancient civilizations made many advances in technology that helped shape our modern world. What inspired, or drove, them to make the advances? For each ancient technological advance named below, explain what forces pushed the given civilization to develop it.

1. wheel

Sumerians: _____

_____

_____

_____

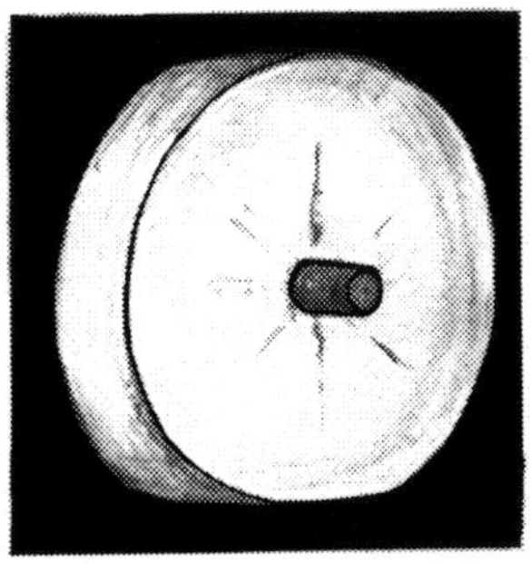

2. chemistry and anatomy

Egyptians: _____

_____

_____

_____

3. surveying and measuring

Egyptians: _____

_____

_____

_____

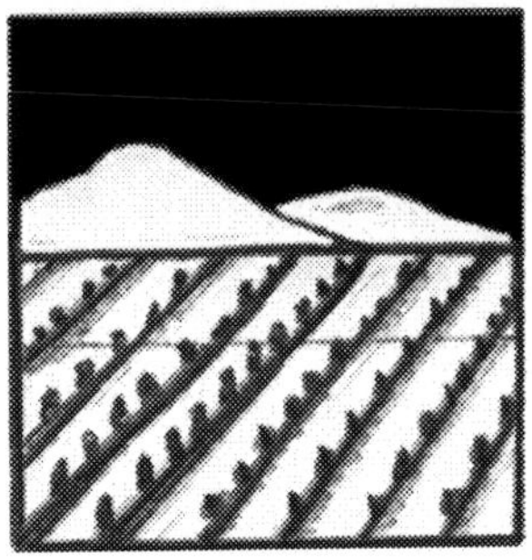

(continued)

The Need for Technology (continued)

4. astronomy and mathematics

Mesopotamians: _____

_____

_____

Olmec, Egyptians, Chinese: _____

_____

_____

5. architecture and engineering

Mesopotamians, Chinese, Egyptians, Olmec:

_____

_____

Indus Valley people: _____

_____

_____

Challenge Question: Which later ancient civilizations and peoples developed the technologies listed below?

alphabet: _____

government-issued coins: _____

Origins of Writing

Directions: The development of writing is one mark of civilization. Ancient people developed several different types of writing systems. Label the examples below with the correct term and civilization. Then tell what was the original, primary use of each writing system for its civilization.

Types: cuneiform, character writing, hieroglyphics

1.

Type: _____

Civilization: _____

Original, primary use: _____

_____

3.

Type: _____

Civilization: _____

Original, primary use: _____

_____

2.

Type: _____

Civilization: _____

Original, primary use: _____

_____

Challenge Question: What do you think may have been some limitations of these early Eurasian writing systems?

Extra Challenge: Investigate the Indus Valley writing system. Scientists have not yet been able to decipher its symbols.

Focus on World History:
The Era of Early Civilizations and Empires

The Mighty Gilgamesh

Directions: *The Epic of Gilgamesh* is an ancient Mesopotamian epic poem about an early king, Gilgamesh, ruler of Uruk. It's a story of fierce battles, larger-than-life heroes, sex, death, and a dangerous journey. The epic tells us a lot about ancient Mesopotamian rulers and their societies. Here are some excerpts from it. Read the excerpts and answer the question that follows each one.

First, the epic introduces us to Gilgamesh.

> He [Gilgamesh] ordered built the walls of Uruk. . . .
> Gilgamesh endured everything harsh,
> He overpowered famous, powerful kings.
> He is a butting bull, the strongest one of all.
> He leads his army and protects its rear guard.
> He is a flood that washes away the walls of enemy cities. . . .
> Two thirds of him is divine, one third human.

1. How does the excerpt above express the Mesopotamian ideal of a king?

_____

_____

Next, Gilgamesh sends a priestess to tame the "hairy-bodied wild man" Enkidu, who lives with the grassland animals. Once Enkidu has been intimate with the woman, his life begins to change.

> Seeing Enkidu, the animals of the grasslands fled.
> Enkidu's body had grown weak; he could not follow the creatures.
> Yet his mind had grown wider, had gained knowledge. . . .
> The woman said to him, to Enkidu:
> "You have become wise, like a god.
> Why did you roam the wilderness with wild animals?
> Come with me to the city, to Uruk. . . ."
> Then Enkidu, with new knowledge in his heart, longed for a friend. . . .
> The woman took off part of her clothing and covered him.
> She took his hand and led him like a child to the camp of the shepherds. . . .
> They set cooked food before him, and strong wine.
> Enkidu stared at it. He had not known about these things before.
> The woman said, "Eat and drink, Enkidu. This is the custom of men."
> Enkidu ate his fill and drank the wine, seven goblets.
> He became like a child; his heart became light.
> He washed his hairy body and was massaged with oil.

(continued)

Focus on World History:
The Era of Early Civilizations and Empires

The Mighty Gilgamesh (continued)

2. What aspects of Mesopotamian history and culture does this passage tell about—not literally, but in a figurative way?

_____

_____

Enkidu arrives in Uruk as a wedding is being celebrated. He challenges Gilgamesh's right to sleep with the bride before her new husband does.

> Enkidu blocked the threshold with his foot, not letting Gilgamesh in.
> They wrestled with one another, like wild bulls with horns locked.
> They shook the walls and shattered the doorposts.
> They wrestled and staggered, and Gilgamesh
> Forced the wild man Enkidu to his knees.
> The rage of Gilgamesh abated and he turned away.

3. What does the fight express about the relationship of Mesopotamian people with their ruler? (Think of Enkidu as representing the Mesopotamian people.)

_____

_____

The fight makes Gilgamesh and Enkidu fast friends. Now they challenge the terrifying demon, named Humbaba, that the gods have set in place to guard the cedar forest.

> Enlil [a chief god] has set Humbaba to guard the cedar forest,
> To terrify mankind, to terrify anyone who goes up to the forest.
> His roar is the storm-flood, his mouth is fire,
> His breath is death. . . .
> Weakness will overcome anyone who goes up to the forest.

4. What does the excerpt about Humbaba tell you about Mesopotamian religious beliefs?

_____

_____

Extra Challenge: Read the entire *Epic of Gilgamesh*. How does the challenge to Humbaba turn out? What more do you learn about Mesopotamian culture and beliefs from the epic?

Marks of Civilization

Directions: The chart below has a list of characteristics that apply to most civilizations. Fill in the chart for one ancient civilization by identifying specific elements of that civilization that match each of the listed characteristics.

Chosen civilization: _____

Complex, well-organized government	
Division of social classes	
Cities and monumental buildings	
Advanced technical skills	
Division of labor	
Writing and record-keeping systems	
Complex religion and religious rituals	
Advanced intellectual and artistic skills	

42   *Focus on World History:*
The Era of Early Civilizations and Empires

Civilizations Spread and Change

The objective of this unit is to help students understand the spread and change of civilizations in the millennia after the emergence of the early river valley civilizations. The years after 2000 B.C.E. saw the development of agricultural societies and civilizations outside the river valleys, in southwestern Asia, the Aegean, Africa, and Europe. At the same time, many people migrated from central and western Asia into parts of India, Southwest Asia, and the Mediterranean. The result was a great mixing of populations and cultures, further connected by widespread trade.

A variety of societies arose in Southwest Asia, including the Babylonians, Hittites, Assyrians, Hebrews, and the quintessential Mediterranean traders, the Phoenicians. Nubia was a rich and varied culture that served as a bridge between northern and sub-Saharan Africa. The Aegean basin saw the development of Cretan and Mycenaean civilizations. In India, Aryans ended the Indus Valley civilizations and brought new ways of life and divisions to that region. Celts spread through and dominated Europe. This unit's activities are designed to draw students into a better understanding of the diversity and expansion during these years of history.

Student Activities

Ancient Trade Networks uses mapping to make students familiar with the trade routes and trade items of the ancient world.

Your Trading Expedition has students put themselves into the place of a Southeast Asian trader and plan their trading expedition, using the guidelines on the worksheet. The Extra Challenge asks students to write an account of or a series of journal entries about their trading expedition.

Nubia: African Crossroads uses a map to make students familiar with the civilization of Nubia. The Extra Challenge invites students to add appropriate dates to a brief time line of Nubian history.

Women of Mesopotamia presents laws from Assyria and Babylonia relating to women, which students use to analyze the difference in the status of women in those societies. Students extend the activity by preparing a chart that summarizes the status of women in a variety of ancient cultures.

War Technology 1 presents an aspect of the use of technology that has had a great influence on human society. Students tell why each invention was an advance over earlier technology.

Moving Populations—a very important aspect of this time in history—lists five different possible types of population movements and has students identify and describe at least one example from ancient history for each. The Extra Challenge asks students to put themselves in the place of an ancient person in a particular society and describe the changes in their world when new people invaded.

The Celts presents Greek and Roman descriptions of the Celtic people. Students do some research into Celtic society and then analyze the question of whether the Celts were "civilized" or "barbarian."

Religious Beliefs helps students recognize the different religious beliefs of ancient people by asking them to identify which society they would probably have been a member of if they held each of the specific listed beliefs. The Extra Challenge asks students to identify ancient religions that practiced human sacrifice or bull worship.

Copper, Bronze, and Iron has students role-play as they explain the advantages and problems of moving into the use of new metals, based on some facts presented on the sheet as well as textbook and background reading.

Civilizations Spread and Change

c. 2000 B.C.E. to 500 B.C.E.

Human societies, like nature, are never static. They always change over time. The first civilizations had developed in river valleys in Africa and Asia. In the years after 2000 B.C.E., civilizations spread through a much wider area. They changed as they grew.

- Groups of nomadic peoples left central and western Asia. They moved into parts of India, southwest Asia, and the Mediterranean region.

- Iron weapons made warfare more deadly. They helped one group after another to invade and take over existing societies.

- New kingdoms emerged, and some early empires formed.

- Trade flourished. It flowed back and forth from Southeast Asia to India to Southwest Asia and the Mediterranean.

The result of all this trade, migration, and invasion was a mixing of cultures and lifestyles. Mixing was most active in the Middle East and Mediterranean regions. People adopted and adapted many things from one another. They shared styles of art, ways of thinking, and techniques of making things. (Meanwhile, people in much of the rest of the world quietly continued their old ways. They kept their hunting-gathering and simple farming ways of life. Trade, though, often brought them into some contact with other cultures.)

Periods in Mesopotamian History

Sumerian c. 3000–2300 B.C.E.
Old Babylonian c. 1900–1600 B.C.E.
Hittites c. 1650–1200 B.C.E.
Hebrews c. 1275–586 B.C.E.
Phoenicians c. 1000–700 B.C.E.
Assyrians c. 900–612 B.C.E.
Persians c. 550–331 B.C.E.

Western Asia

Western Asia, or the Middle East, saw a great deal of cultural mixing in the second and first millenniums B.C.E. The Sumerians developed the first civilization in this area. Then a new people known as Babylonians took control. One of their rulers, Hammurabi, expanded the kingdom and set up a well-ordered law code. Babylonian culture was a lot like the culture of Sumer.

Around 1600 B.C.E., a new people swept into the region. These Hittites had originally been nomadic herders. They had lived in the grasslands of central Asia, north of the Black and Caspian seas. They brought two very important new technologies to the people they conquered. The Hittites knew how to make and use iron weapons and horse-drawn chariots.

Hittite power faded around 1200 B.C.E. After the Hittites, around 900 B.C.E., came the

(continued)

Civilizations Spread and Change (continued)

Assyrians. These warlike people were fiercely aggressive and powerful. They created the world's first real empire. They controlled lands from Iran in the east to the Mediterranean in the west. Their rule also reached south into Egypt. The Assyrians kept strict control of the diverse people they conquered. To achieve control, they used terror tactics and forced migrations. They often moved entire peoples out of their homeland and made them settle in other parts of the empire. Thanks to the Assyrians, millions of people made new homes all through western Asia.

Assyrians

Two other groups in western Asia played a notable role. The Hebrews were at first a group of nomadic herders. Around 1275 B.C.E., they left Egypt, where they had lived for several centuries. They wandered for years. They settled at last in a strip of land along the Mediterranean coast known as Palestine. The Hebrews worked out a detailed code of laws. They also developed one of the world's great religions, Judaism. (You'll learn more about that in Unit 6.)

The Phoenicians lived in another strip of land along the Mediterranean. Their region was just north of the Hebrews'. The Phoenicians were great seafarers. Their country, Phoenicia, was tiny. Even so, these people built colonies and trade routes along the entire length and breadth of the Mediterranean Sea. Phoenician traders may have sailed as far as Britain for tin. They may also have voyaged far down the west coast of Africa. One part of Phoenician culture plays a large part in our lives today. Phoenicians worked out the first form of the alphabet that is the basis of modern Western writing systems.

Africa: Egypt and Nubia

Around 1640 B.C.E., an Asian people called Hyksos invaded Egypt. They struck across the isthmus of Suez. The Hyksos used horse-drawn chariots to defeat the foot soldiers of the Egyptian army. Although the Hyksos adopted Egyptian culture, the Egyptians themselves did not accept them. The New Kingdom rulers of Egypt expelled the Hyksos around 1550 B.C.E. Then these rulers took control of lands to the east and south. This made it easier to defend Egypt

(continued)

Civilizations Spread and Change *(continued)*

from invasion. The new lands also added valuable natural resources and taxes. These boosted the wealth of Egypt's upper classes.

The land to the south that Egypt took control of was known as Nubia. The Egyptians often called it Kush. Nubia lay along the upper Nile River and had rich deposits of gold. It had long been a vital trade route. It linked the Mediterranean region and tropical Africa south of the Sahara Desert. Nubia had developed its own distinctive civilization. During the period of Egyptian control, Nubian culture absorbed many elements of Egyptian art, religion, and language. Egyptian control of Nubia ended after 1200 B.C.E. Then Nubians ruled Egypt from around 715 to 660 B.C.E. The last Nubian kingdom, Meroë, collapsed around 300 C.E.

Europe: Cretans, Greeks, and Celts

Another culture developed on an island in the Mediterranean Sea called Crete. This civilization was called Cretan, for its island center.

It is also called Minoan, for its famous king, Minos. It began developing before 2000 B.C.E. and flourished between 1600 and 1400 B.C.E.

Like the Phoenicians, the Cretans were highly skilled seafarers and traded widely. They built great palaces and an elaborate labyrinth (maze) related to bull-worship. Colorful wall paintings record their way of life, including groups of women enjoying Cretan amusements. The civilization of Crete was destroyed around 1400 B.C.E. The cause might have been invading Greeks. Or a natural disaster might have erased this culture.

Next to Crete, on the European mainland, was Greece. Peoples from the north migrated into this region starting around 2000 B.C.E. They mingled with the native population to form a new culture. One of their earliest cities was Mycenae. So these people are now called the Mycenaean Greeks. Like the Phoenicians and Cretans before them, these Greeks became skilled ancient-world traders. They faded from prominence by around 1100 B.C.E.

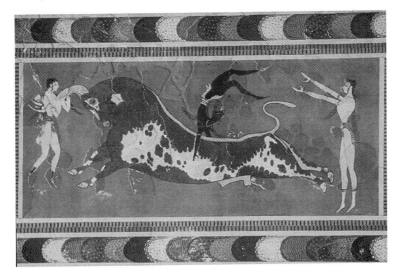

(continued)

Civilizations Spread and Change *(continued)*

People called Celts migrated west from central Europe starting sometime after 1000 B.C.E. They soon became the dominant culture in Europe north of the Alps. They built hilltop forts and traded with Greeks and, later, Romans. Celts loved war and battle. Their priests, called Druids, guided the all-important rituals of Celtic life. They also acted as judges. Celtic women had more rights than most other women of their time. They were also admired for their aggressive and feisty nature.

India and China

India also went through changes after its early civilization-forming period. As in western Asia, a new people invaded from the grasslands of central Asia. These Aryans arrived in about 1500 B.C.E. They replaced the Indus Valley city civilizations with a herding culture. But the Aryans had settled in a very fertile area. So after a number of years they settled down to a farming way of life. The Aryans were fairly light-skinned. The Indian peoples they invaded were darker-skinned. The Aryans tended to stay in the north. The people they displaced moved to the south. This division led to the building of strict class divisions in Indian society. (You will learn more about this in Unit 6.)

China moved along a different path. It was not much affected by mixing with other cultures. China was active in the long-distance trade of the times. But it was isolated by geography. Also, it had developed a sophisticated and self-sufficient culture. Nomadic horse-culture tribal people did invade from time to time. But they made no great inroads into Chinese territory or culture.

Ancient Trade Networks

Directions: Trade was a very important aspect of life in ancient times. On your map of the ancient world, draw lines to show the following land and sea trade routes. Also, locate and label the named places and bodies of water. Then add symbols to the map to indicate the sources of the highly prized trade goods of ancient times listed below. (Create your own symbols and make a key to them by drawing each symbol next to its name on the list below.)

Palace of Nebuchadnezzar, Babylon, Iraq

Trade Routes

1. Mesopotamia (Damascus, Antioch, Babylon) —> northern Iran —> central Asia (Merv, Bukhara, Samarkand, Kashgar) —> Tarim Basin (north or south route) —> North China plain (Chang'an, Luoyang, Pacific Ocean)

2. China via South China Sea —> Southeast Asia —> across Isthmus of Kra and (alternative) through Strait of Malacca —> India east coast —> between India and Sri Lanka —> directly across Arabian Sea and up Red Sea and down along East Africa —> (alternative) up India west coast, then up Persian Gulf or across Arabian Sea

Trade Goods and Regions of Origin

copper (Morocco, Spain, Caucasus)

tin (Spain, Britain, central Europe, Caucasus)

silver (Spain, Caucasus)

amber (northern Europe)

wool (Asia Minor)

timber (Asia Minor, Phoenicia-Syria-Lebanon)

glass (Phoenicia)

textiles (Middle East)

papyrus (Egypt)

linen (Egypt)

gold (Nubia)

ivory (Nubia, India)

resins (south of Nubia, southern Arabia)

spices (India, Spice Islands [Indonesia])

oil (Crete, Greece)

wine (Crete, Greece)

silk (China)

tea (China)

citrus fruit (China)

purple cloth (Phoenicia)

exotic woods (Southeast Asia)

Your Trading Expedition

Directions: Imagine you are a trader based in Southeast Asia. Plan a trading expedition you are going to make to the Mediterranean region. Write up your plan below.

1. Time of year you will travel (take into account the monsoons): _____
   _____

2. Route you will take (include its approximate length in miles and months if you can):
   _____
   _____

3. Means of transportation: _____
   _____

4. Trade goods you will bring with you: _____
   _____

5. Markets where you will sell your goods: _____
   _____

6. Things you will bring back with you: _____
   _____

7. Difficulties/special occurrences you need to be alert to: _____
   _____

Extra Challenge: Write an account of your journey after you return to your home base. Or, write a series of journal entries as you go along on the trading expedition.

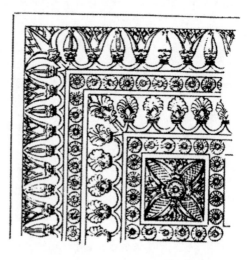

Focus on World History:
The Era of Early Civilizations and Empires

Nubia: African Crossroads

Nubia was a powerful African kingdom that lay along the upper (southern) Nile River valley. Also called Kush, it was located in present-day northern Sudan and southern Egypt. This activity sheet will help you learn more about Nubia.

Directions: Study the map and find information on Nubia. Then answer the questions.

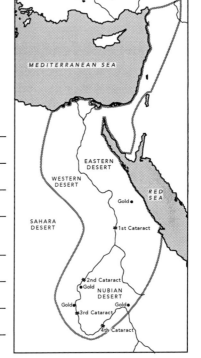

1. Why was Nubia a natural trade corridor? _____

   _____

   _____

   _____

2. Why was Nubia wealthy? _____

   _____

   _____

   _____

   _____

3. What obstacles existed to travel through Nubia? _____

   _____

   _____

   _____

Extra Challenge: Listed below are significant events in the history of Nubia. Fill in the date for each event.

c. _____ B.C.E.   Egypt takes control of Nubia.

c. _____ B.C.E.   Nubia takes control of Egypt.

c. _____ B.C.E.   Assyrians sweep into Egypt, push out Nubians.

c. _____ B.C.E.   Meroë becomes Nubian capital and a great iron-producing center.

c. _____ C.E.   Axum invades and destroys Nubia.

---

51   *Focus on World History:*
                                                                                        The Era of Early Civilizations and Empires

Women of Mesopotamia

The status of women varied among the many different societies of ancient times. Here are laws relating to women, some from Babylon and the others from Assyria.

Babylonian law, Code of Hammurabi, c. 1800 B.C.E.

If a man's wife be surprised with another man, both shall be tied and thrown into the water, but the husband may pardon his wife.

If a man wishes to separate from a woman who has borne him children, or from his wife who has borne him children, then he shall give that wife her dowry, and a part of the yield of field, garden, and property, so that she can rear her children. When she has brought up her children, a portion of all that is given to the children, equal as that of one son, shall be given to her. She may then marry the man of her heart.

If a man wishes to separate from his wife who has borne him no children, he shall give her the amount of her purchase money and the dowry which she brought from her father's house, and let her go.

If a man strikes a free-born woman so that she loses her unborn child, he shall pay ten shekels for her loss.

Assyrian law, c. 800 B.C.E.

If a man has caught a man with his wife and has then brought a charge against him and proved it against him, both of them shall be put to death; there is no guilt in this.

A man may flog his wife, pull out her hair, split and injure her ears; there is no guilt in this.

If a woman shall give shelter to a wife who is running away from her husband, both women shall have their ears cut off.

Directions: Explain what differences in the status of Babylonian and Assyrian women these laws express. Then, prepare a chart that summarizes the status of women in the ancient societies you have been studying.

War Technology 1

Directions: Human beings use advances in technology to improve people's lives. They also use advances in technology to make war more efficient and deadly. For each item of war technology listed below, tell why it was an advance over earlier technology.

1. use of iron: _____

_____

_____

_____

2. composite bow: _____

_____

_____

_____

3. siege machinery (mobile towers, battering rams): _____

_____

4. chariot warfare: _____

_____

5. cavalry warfare (soldiers, with weapons, mounted on horses): _____

_____

6. cataphracts (specially bred extra-large horses): _____

_____

7. stirrups: _____

_____

Extra Challenge: Find out which people first developed each innovation above.

Focus on World History:
The Era of Early Civilizations and Empires

Moving Populations

Directions: Migrations, raids, invasions—all had a great impact on ancient societies. Peoples and cultures mixed, creating mutual changes. Listed below are possible types of population movements. For each, identify at least one example from ancient history and briefly describe it.

1. invade, and build an empire

   Example: _____

   Description: _____

   _____

2. invade, plunder and destroy, move on

   Example: _____

   Description: _____

3. invade, and mix with the settled people of the area

   Example: _____

   Description: _____

4. invade, settle, but remain separate from the people who were there before

   Example: _____

   Description: _____

5. raid, then return to your home territory

   Example: _____

   Description: _____

Extra Challenge: Become a person who lives in Mesopotamia, India, Egypt, Nubia, China, or the Aegean world. Describe the changes in your world when new people invaded.

The Celts

In western Europe, a very different people were spreading and developing their culture. These people were called the Celts (*kelts*). Both the Greeks and, later, the Romans encountered the Celts and were very interested in them. Greek and Roman writers have left us some vivid descriptions. Here are some of those descriptions.

> The whole race is war mad and both high-spirited and always eager for battle, although otherwise straightforward and not uncouth. When they are stirred up they assemble in their bands for battle, quite openly and without forethought, so that they are easily outwitted by those who plan the battle. They are ready to fight with nothing on their side but their own strength and courage.

> Nearly all of the Gauls [Celts] are tall, fair and have a ruddy complexion, seem terrible from the sternness of their eyes, and are very quarrelsome and have great pride and insolence. A whole troop of foreigners would not be able to withstand a single Gaul if he called to his assistance his wife, who is usually very strong and with blue eyes.

> Throughout Gaul only two classes are of any account and enjoy any distinction. The masses are treated almost as slaves, exercise no self-initiative, and are never consulted about policy. The great part, when crushed by debt or heavy taxation or oppressed by powerful individuals, bind themselves in slavery to the nobles, who exercise over them all the rights masters have over slaves. One of the two classes consists of the Druids [priests], the other of the Knights [chief warriors].

> When they become drunk, they fall into a stupor or into a maniacal rage. At dinner they tend to be moved by casual remarks to wordy arguments and, after a challenge, to fight in single combat, regarding their lives as of little consequence.

> In war, every single step the Celts took was guided by the heat of passion rather than by cool calculation. Their battle-cry was so overwhelming, it seemed that not only the trumpets and the soldiers but all the country round had got a voice and caught up the cry.

Directions: The excerpts above were all written by ancient Greek observers and by later ancient Romans who conquered the Celtic lands. Are these observations accurate? Do some research into Celtic society, and then answer this question: Were the Celts a "civilized" people, or were they the "barbarians" that the Greeks and Romans labeled them as?

55   *Focus on World History:*
                                                                         The Era of Early Civilizations and Empires

Religious Beliefs

Directions: Ancient peoples held a wide variety of religious beliefs. Which ancient society or societies might you have been a member of if you had held each of the religious beliefs described below? Choose from among these societies as they existed about 2000–500 B.C.E.

Babylonian	Chinese	Hebrew	Phoenician
Celtic	Egyptian	Nubian	Sumerian

1. You hold your ancestors in great reverence. _____

2. You bury your dead in shaft graves that go deep underground. _____

3. You sacrifice your own child to appease your angry gods. _____

4. You see life after death as gloomy and hopeless, in the Land of No Return.
_____

5. You revere the sun god above all other deities. _____

6. You worship only one god, an angry desert deity. _____

7. The spirits answer your questions through oracle bones. _____

8. You worship both northern and southern African deities. _____

9. You believe that the human head, as the dwelling place of the soul, has mysterious powers.
_____

10. You fear your uncaring and fickle gods._____

11. You believe in life after death, after a long journey for the departed soul, but only for persons who led a good, truthful life. _____

Extra Challenge: Create a chart that shows which ancient religions practiced human sacrifice, and for what purpose. Or do the same for ancient religions that practiced a form of bull worship.

Copper, Bronze, and Iron

Directions: Technology advanced in important ways as people learned to use different kinds of metals. Read the basic facts about copper, bronze, and iron below. Using that and other information from your reading, role-play the roles described with a classmate.

> **Copper:** naturally occurring metal, can be extracted from ore by simple smelting
> **Bronze:** metal made by mixing molten copper and tin, both naturally occurring metals in some but not all areas where bronze was used
> **Iron:** metal extracted from ore in a complex process, then hammered or cast into shape

1. You are a Neolithic toolmaker. Explain to your young apprentice the advantages of making and using copper tools rather than stone tools. Respond to your apprentice's concerns.

   As the apprentice, point out the drawbacks of copper use.

2. You are an artisan in Shang China. Describe to your patron the beautiful objects you plan to make for her out of bronze. Show her some examples of bronze works you have made in the past, pointing out their special features. Respond to her concerns.

   As the patron, express your concerns about getting the raw material for this artwork.

3. You are a Hittite army leader. Make the case to your ruler about the advantages of using iron weapons. Respond to the ruler's concerns.

   As the ruler, express your concerns about whether switching to the complex iron-smelting process is worth the extra time and expense involved.

4. You are a government official in charge of agriculture in Zhou China. You want to introduce iron farming tools to your country. Explain to your superior the advantages of using iron tools. Also, explain the superior method of producing cast iron that only China has so far developed.

   As the superior, ask about the cost-effectiveness and usefulness of this proposal.

Greeks and Persians

The objective of this unit is to help students understand the achievements and lasting importance of Greek civilization and the interactions of Greek and Persian societies and cultures. Greece developed a classical culture whose institutions, ways of thought, and cultural styles influenced people throughout the ancient world and endured for centuries. Influential aspects of Greek culture remain in evidence today, for example, in architecture and the concept of democracy, and Greek science—although lost to most of the world for centuries—pioneered many groundbreaking ideas and concepts.

The clash between Greeks and Persians culminated in the conquests of Alexander of Macedon, which resulted in the largest empire yet known in the world and in the melding of Greek and Eurasian culture throughout that empire. This unit's activities are designed to draw students into a better understanding of the events and significance of the years of Greek and Persian ascendancy.

Student Activities

Mapping Ancient Greece uses mapping to familiarize students with Greek geography, the significance of specific Greek sites, and the ways in which Greek geography affected the Greek way of life.

A Greek Science Fair provides ideas about Greek scientific findings that students could demonstrate at a class science fair.

Greek Life in Today's Language shows students how the influence of Greek life remains in our lives today by having them explain the specific Greek history origin of a list of words we use in English today. The Extra Challenge continues the exercise with more advanced vocabulary words.

Greek Women invites students to summarize and think about the very different status of Athenian and Spartan women, both free and slave.

The Plague in Athens presents a first-person account of a plague that hit Athens in 430 B.C.E. Students trace the progress of the epidemic on a map and answer questions to understand the impact of the plague and conditions that made ancient cities especially vulnerable to epidemic diseases.

Alexander and Hellenization presents a contemporary account of a mass marriage ceremony between Greeks and Persians to draw students into an examination of the deliberate Hellenization policy of Alexander and its consequences. The Extra Challenge invites students to imagine themselves as participants in this ceremony and the ways in which they might react to the differences between Greek and Persian culture.

Persians Versus Greeks presents words of advice (real or imagined) reported by Herodotus relating to Persian aggression against Greece. Students use these excerpts to identify weaknesses of the invading Persian army and key characteristics of Greek societies that enabled them to resist successfully.

The First Historians presents excerpts from Herodotus and Thucydides to introduce students to the methods developed by the earliest historians. The Extra Challenge asks students to write a "history" essay using speeches in the way that Herodotus and Thucydides did.

Greeks and Persians

c. 600 B.C.E. to 200 B.C.E.

Greek City-States

The history of early Greek civilization is closely tied to Greek geography. Greece is a land surrounded on three sides by the sea. Many islands lie in the oceans nearby. The mainland is cut up by short mountain ranges and nearly cut in two by a long arm of the western sea. The land is dry and rocky, with not much fertile farmland, although olive trees and grapevines flourish there. Greece has no major rivers, few metal deposits, and little timber.

Because of these facts of geography, the Greeks became sea traders. The seas, and many natural harbors, encouraged trade. The land couldn't produce enough food to support a growing population. Trade would bring the needed food supplies, plus metal and timber. Also, as populations grew, Greek people left their homeland. They settled on the many islands and established new settlements all around the Mediterranean. Sea trade kept the scattered Greek populations in touch with one another.

Mountains separated most Greek settlements from one another. So each developed into a city-state, or *polis*—an urban center and its surrounding rural plains. Each city had an *acropolis*, a fortified high point, and an *agora*, an open-air public gathering place.

Powerful Greek city-states began to rise in about 750 B.C.E. Kings assisted by nobles ruled them. Then councils of nobles took over from the kings. This was rule by **aristocracy**. From around 650 to 500 B.C.E., many city-states were ruled by individual tyrants. (*Tyrant* at this time meant a person who seized power by force.) These tyrants gave political power to the merchant classes instead of to the corrupt and arrogant nobles.

In time, each tyrant family was overthrown. The new government sometimes went back into the hands of the upper classes. More often, **democracy** became the new governing method. In this form, all citizens participated in running the city-state.

(continued)

Greeks and Persians (continued)

The two most prominent Greek city-states were Athens and Sparta. Sparta was a militaristic society. Spartans had conquered neighboring people in southern Greece. The Spartans reduced them to the status of slaves, or *helots*. Sparta was constantly in fear of a helot uprising. So the Spartan way of life revolved around military preparedness. Boys and men devoted their lives to the military. Girls and women devoted their lives to producing new generations of strong soldiers. The arts, commerce, and foreign travel did not exist in Sparta.

Athens developed quite differently. While the city itself was inland, it had access to its own port of Piraeus. Athenians became expert sea traders. As trade flourished, the wealth and power of Athens increased. Its rulers built beautiful public buildings and temples. A series of reform-minded rulers made Athens into the world's first true democracy:

- Draco drew up a code of laws.
- Solon ended slavery for debtors. He gave voting rights to more people.
- Pisastratus let nonlandowners become citizens. He gave nobles' lands to landless peasants.
- Cleisthenes ended class divisions based on wealth. He made all male citizens members of the voting Assembly.

By 450 B.C.E., all political power in Athens belonged to bodies that all citizens could take part in. A Council of Five Hundred proposed laws. An Assembly voted on laws. Court cases were decided by juries of the people.

However, democracy in Athens had a serious restriction. Only citizens could take part, and only free men with Athenian parents could be citizens. Many free men who lived in Athens were considered aliens. They were not eligible to become citizens. Slaves and women were never citizens.

The Persian-Greek Conflict

While the Greeks were developing their civilization, a new empire was forming in the ancient land of Persia (today's Iran). This land linked southwest Asia (the Middle East) with southern and central Asia. Persia was bordered by mountains at the edges. Its environment was generally harsh.

Around 550 B.C.E. a great ruler named Cyrus united the area under his rule. He then took over the rest of Asia Minor. Cyrus and his successors created a vast and complex empire. It included many different peoples with a great variety of social systems. For the most part, the Persian rulers allowed these many peoples to live according to their usual customs and laws. Many Persians followed the religion of Zoroastrianism. It is named for Zoroaster, who is credited with writing the hymns that express the religion's beliefs. Zoroastrianism saw human history as a vast struggle between good and evil. It believed in one supreme god and an afterlife achieved by people who led ethical lives.

(continued)

Focus on World History:
The Era of Early Civilizations and Empires

Greeks and Persians *(continued)*

Part of the area Cyrus conquered included Greek city-states across the Aegean Sea from the Greek mainland. These city-states revolted against Persian rule, under Cyrus and his successor Darius. The city-states on the Greek mainland helped these revolts. This gave rise to a mutual enmity between Greek city-states and Persian rulers. A series of wars resulted. Greek cities were badly damaged but fought off the Persian attempt to take them over and survived. Athens emerged as the leader of the Greek world. Democratic city-states had won over the traditional king-god type of empire or kingdom.

Classic Greek Culture

Once the Persian threat no longer existed, Athens became the leading city of Greece. It developed a culture that had a lasting impact on the world. Some highlights of Greek culture include the following:

- Three great thinkers—Socrates, Plato, and Aristotle—developed lasting philosophies of life.

- Greek mathematicians (Pythagoras, Euclid) established the principles of geometry.

- Hippocrates learned so much about disease and health that he earned the nickname "Father of Medicine."

- Democritus speculated that all matter is made up of moving atoms.

- Aristarchus believed that the earth and other planets revolved around the sun.

Unfortunately, these advances in science were lost to the Western world and not rediscovered until many centuries later.

Socrates

In the arts and literature, Herodutus and Thucydides created the role of historian, a person who records past events. Greek playwrights created the traditions of drama and comedy in the theater. Aeschylus, Sophocles, and Euripedes wrote drama (serious plays). Aristophanes penned comedies. We can still read these plays, see them performed today, and relate to the human feelings and dilemmas they depict. Greek architecture and sculpture developed forms we still see today.

(continued)

Greeks and Persians *(continued)*

Alexander and the Macedonian Age

In 431 B.C.E. the very different Greek city-states of Athens and Sparta descended into a war. They fought each other for control of the Greek world. This Peloponnesian war went on for about 30 years. It lowered morale in all the Greek city-states. Meanwhile, a new power arose in the northern Greek area of Macedonia. The Macedonian ruler Philip II developed an impressive fighting force. With it, he took over Greece, weakened by the Peloponnesian war. Philip was assassinated in 336 B.C.E. His son, Alexander, was only 20 years old. He seemed much too young to continue Philip's expansion by conquest. But Alexander proved to be one of history's great conquerors and generals. He extended Macedonian control into Asia. He took over Persia and created the greatest empire yet known.

Alexander's empire didn't last long. It split up after Alexander's early death in 323 B.C.E. at the age of 33 (after many rowdy nights of carousing). But Alexander's empire had an enduring impact on the world. Greek culture spread through all the land Alexander took over. This added aspects of Greek thought, art, and science to native cultures throughout Alexander's realm. Three generals split up the empire among themselves after Alexander's death. They continued to promote Greek culture in their realms. This is now called **Hellenistic** culture, after the term Greeks sometimes used for themselves, Hellenes.

The Parthenon

Focus on World History:
The Era of Early Civilizations and Empires

Mapping Ancient Greece

Directions: On your map of Greece, locate and label the following items. Where indicated, provide brief information about each place name.

Pindus Mountains	Attica	Peloponnesus
Taygetos Mountains	Macedonia	Aegean Sea
Hellespont	Ionia	Ionian Sea
Gulf of Corinth	Crete	Mediterranean Sea

1. Mt. Olympus: _____

2. Delphi: _____

3. Olympia: _____

4. Athens: _____

5. Sparta: _____

6. Troy: _____

7. Lesbos: _____

8. Rhodes: _____

9. Salamis: _____

10. Marathon: _____

11. Plataea: _____

Extra Challenge: Explain how Greek geography affected the Greek way of life.

A Greek Science Fair

Directions: Greek scientists made many discoveries. And they experimented with many scientific principles. With classmates, create a Greek "science fair" to demonstrate and show results of Greek scientific inquiry. Here are some important Greek findings you might want to consider for your science fair.

the lever, block and tackle (Archimedes)

the "magic pitcher" (Hero)

pulley and weight gadgets (Philon)

the water screw (Archimedes)

the lighthouse (Pharos)

density by displacement of water (Archimedes)

calculation of the circumference and diameter of the earth (Eratosthenes)

geometric principles (Pythagoras, Hippocrates, Appolonius, Euclid)

astronomy observations (Anaxagoras, Eudoxus, Aristarchus, Hipparchus, Ptolemy)

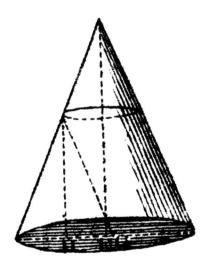

Focus on World History:
The Era of Early Civilizations and Empires

Greek Life in Today's Language

Directions: People, places, and events in ancient Greece have found their way into the words we use today in the English language. Build your vocabulary by using what you know about Greek history. Explain the meaning and the Greek history origin of each of the modern words listed below.

1. **attic**—Meaning: _____

   Greek origin: Attica _____

2. **cynic**—Meaning: _____

   Greek origin: Cynics _____

3. **epicurean**—Meaning: _____

   Greek origin: Epicurus _____

4. **marathon**—Meaning: _____

   Greek origin: Marathon _____

5. **pyrrhic** (victory)—Meaning: _____

   Greek origin: Pyrrhus _____

6. **spartan**—Meaning: _____

   Greek origin: Sparta _____

7. **stoic**—Meaning: _____

   Greek origin: Stoics _____

8. **thespian**—Meaning: _____

   Greek origin: Thespis _____

Extra Challenge: Continue this exercise on another sheet by explaining the meaning and Greek history origin of these words: *draconian* (Draco), *laconic* (Laconia), *philippic* (Philip of Macedon), *solon* (Solon), *sophistry* (Sophists), *sybaritic* (Sybaris).

Focus on World History:
                                                                         The Era of Early Civilizations and Empires

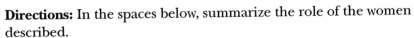

Greek Women

The status of women in Greece varied, by city-state and social class. Socrates, according to Plato, said: "Natural gifts are to be found here and there in both creatures [women and men] alike; and every occupation is open to both, so far as their natures are concerned." However, that was hardly the case in real life.

Directions: In the spaces below, summarize the role of the women described.

1. Free woman of Athens: _____
   _____
   _____

2. Free woman of Sparta: _____
   _____
   _____

3. Slave woman of Athens: _____
   _____
   _____

4. Slave woman of Sparta: _____
   _____
   _____

Further Directions: Think about the differences in Greek women's status that you have summarized. Then explain which one of these four types of women you would choose to be if you were a woman in ancient Greece. Explain the reasons for your choice. Then discuss choices with classmates.

Extra Challenge: (Consider this question after you have read "The Plague in Athens" worksheet.) What particular effect might the epidemic have had on the upper-class women of Athens?

The Plague in Athens

Directions: In 430 B.C.E., a deadly **plague** struck Athens. It rapidly killed off many of the people. Here is a description of the event, written by the Greek historian Thucydides. Read the excerpt and complete the activities below it.

Physicians were of no avail at first, treating the plague as they did, in ignorance of its nature. Nay, they themselves died most of all, because they most visited the sick. Nor was any other human art of any avail. As for the prayers offered in the temples, or appeals to the oracles, and similar efforts, they were all of no use. At last people, overwhelmed by the calamity, gave up all these efforts.

The disease is said to have begun in Ethiopia, south of Egypt. Then it came down into Egypt, and Libya, and spread over the greatest part of the Persian empire. It fell suddenly on the city of Athens, first attacking the people in the port of Piraeus. Afterward it reached the upper city also. . . .

But the most dreadful part of the whole calamity was the dejection felt whenever anyone found himself sickening (immediately falling into a feeling of despair), and the fact of people becoming infected from helping others, and so dying like sheep. Indeed, this caused the greatest mortality among them. If through fear they were unwilling to visit each other, they perished from being deserted. Many houses were empty from the lack of anyone to attend to the sufferers. . . .

The crowding of the people from the country into the city added to the misery. The new-comers had no homes of their own, but lived in huts that were stifling in the summer heat. The mortality among these spread unchecked. Bodies lay on one another in the death-agony, and half-dead creatures rolled about the streets and round all the fountains, longing for water. . . .

The plague also was the origin of lawless conduct in the city, to a greater extent than ever before. . . . People saw the change so sudden for those who were prosperous and quickly perished, and for those who before had had nothing, and at once took possession of the property of the dead. So they resolved to take their enjoyment quickly, and think only of pleasure. . . . Everything that was immediately pleasant, and that brought pleasure by any means whatever, this was laid down to be both honorable and advisable.

1. Trace the progress of the epidemic on your map of the ancient world.

2. Why was this a particularly bad time for the plague to strike Athens?

3. What conditions in Athens helped to make the city especially vulnerable to an epidemic like this?

Alexander and Hellenization

Directions: Once Alexander the Great had conquered Persia, he began to mix Greek culture with Persian culture (and with other cultures of his wide empire). Here is a description of a mass wedding of Alexander and over 80 of his high-ranking officials to Persian brides. (It was written by the Greek historian Chares.) Read it and answer the questions that follow.

After [the victory], Alexander celebrated a marriage feast for himself and his comrades. Ninety-two chambers were reserved for the event. A building was constructed with enough room for one hundred couches. Each couch was made of silver and was covered with expensive wedding decorations. Alexander's own couch had golden feet. Alexander invited all his friends to the banquet and seated them across from him and the other bridegrooms. . . .

The furnishings for the reception room were extremely expensive and magnificent. Sumptuous tapestries hung above carpets of purple and scarlet and gold. . . . As a trumpet sounded, the marriage feast began. It lasted five days.

Alexander the Great

1. Why would Alexander promote intermarriage between Greeks and Persians?

   _____

   _____

2. In what other ways did Alexander merge Greek and Persian cultures? Use the areas listed below to help answer this question.

   clothing: _____

   government: _____

   education of young people: _____

   other intermarriages: _____

   establishment of new cities: _____

Extra Challenge: Imagine you are a Persian bride or a Greek bridegroom at Alexander's wedding feast. What things about your new spouse do you find different from people in your own culture? Do you dislike these differences, or do you find them interesting?

Persians Versus Greeks

In these excerpts, the Greek historian Herodotus gives us words of advice (real or imagined) from advisors to the Persian king Xerxes. Xerxes is preparing to lead his army to conquer Greece in 480 B.C.E. Herodotus also provides an Athenian response to Persian demands to surrender.

Artabanus, on the Persian army's invasion of Greece

O king! I see that the two most important things are opposed to you. . . . The more you add to the size of your army or the number of your ships, the more hostile will those two things become. Those two things are the land and the sea. In all the wide sea there is not anywhere a harbor large enough to receive all your vessels, in case a storm arises, and provide them with sure protection. And yet you will need, not one such harbor only, but many in succession, along the entire Greek coast. . . . The land will also be your enemy. For if no Greeks resist your advance, as you proceed farther and farther, lured on by your success, you will find the land more and more hostile. Should nothing else stop you, the mere distance, becoming greater as time goes on, will at last produce a famine among your troops.

Demaratus, on the Greek character

Poverty has at all times dwelled with us in Greece, while Courage is an ally whom we have gained through wisdom and strict laws. Courage enables us to drive out poverty and escape slavery. . . . The Spartans, when they fight singly, are as good men as any in the world, and when they fight together, are the bravest of all. For though they are freemen, they are not in all respects free. Law is the master they acknowledge, and they fear this master more than your subjects fear you. Whatever the Law commands, they do, and his commandment is always the same. It forbids them to flee in battle, whatever the number of their foes, and requires them to stand firm, and either to conquer or to die.

Response of Athenians to Persian demands to surrender

We know, as well as you do, that the power of the Mede [Persian] is many times greater than our own. . . . Nevertheless we cling so to freedom that we shall offer what resistance we can. . . . We share a common brotherhood with all Greeks: our common language, the altars and rituals of our gods, and our common character.

Directions: In a class discussion, or on a separate sheet, develop answers to these questions: How accurate was Artabanus' prediction about problems with Xerxes' military campaign in Greece? What characteristics of the Greeks might make their armies better coordinated and more effective than the Persian armies? Compare to American history: How might you relate the ancient Athenian response to the eighteenth-century American colonists' response to their British rulers?

The First Historians

The ancient Greeks developed a new type of study that they called *historia*, or "investigation/ research." They collected and recorded information about past events. Thucydides and Herodotus were two of these early historians. They created two different ways of approaching the recording of history.

Herodotus, 5th century B.C.E.

I, Herodotus of Halicarnassus, hereby publish my researches, in the hope of preserving from decay the remembrance of what people have done, and of preventing the great and wonderful actions of the Greeks and the Barbarians from losing their rightful reward of glory; and, as well, to put on record what were the reasons for their feud with one another.

Thucydides, 4th century B.C.E.

[Thucydides quoted long speeches, many of which he had never actually heard, in his histories. Here is his explanation of that.] And as for what various people said, . . . it was hard to remember the exact words of what was said; both for myself, with regard to what I heard in person, and for those who reported it to me. . . . While I kept as closely as possible to the general sense of what was really said, I recorded what I thought the speakers would have said on the matters that came before them. But with regard to the *facts* of what was done in the war, I did not presume to state them on hearsay from any chance informant, nor as I myself thought probably happened. Rather, I stated facts about events at which I was personally present and, when other people informed me about events, I reported those facts only after I investigated them accurately in every particular, as far as was possible.

Directions: Use these excerpts to consider and discuss the role and obligations of the historian. What are the purposes that motivated Herodotus to write his history? What two methods does Thucydides use in recording his history? Do you think Thucydides' use of speeches is a valid approach to writing history? What about current history? Do you think that today's media report events in a complete and unbiased way that future historians will be able to rely on? What would be valid sources today for tomorrow's historians to draw on?

Extra Challenge: Write a "history" essay in which you record the speech of a well-known figure from the past. Use the Thucydides approach of writing what you think the person would have said in some particular situation.

Major Religions and Ethical Systems

The objective of this unit is to make students familiar with the major and enduring religious and ethical systems that, remarkably, all emerged or came to prominence in the period between 1000 B.C.E. and 300 C.E. Judaism, Vedic religion/Hinduism, Buddhism, Christianity, Confucianism, and Daoism all emerged during these times, and each was adopted by many people. (Islam emerged in the 600s C.E. and is examined in detail in book 2 of this series.) Judaism and Christianity developed in south-west Asia, Hinduism and Buddhism in India, and Confucianism and Daoism in China.

Each of these belief systems spread and united people of diverse political and ethnic identities and promoted the interchange of cultures throughout the varied regions of the world. This unit's activities are designed to draw students into a better understanding of the differences and similarities among these different religions and belief systems and their lasting influence in the world today.

Student Activities

The Bhagavad Gita presents portions of the classic Indian epic poem and asks students to identify basic characteristics of Hindu religious beliefs and society as expressed in the excerpts.

The Buddhist Path presents students with two Buddhist ways to find and follow the path to right living, with an exercise and questions to help students analyze these aspects of Buddhism.

The Ten Commandments presents students with the Ten Commandments of the Hebrew (and also Christian) religion. Students compare these with the previous Buddhist Eightfold Path and guidelines for right conduct. The Extra Challenge asks students to role-play a discussion among Jesus Christ, the Buddha, Confucius, and Moses, the representative of the Judaic god.

The Christian Ideal presents the ideals of Christian behavior as expressed by Jesus Christ and recorded in the New Testament. Students identify the ways in which Jesus elaborated on the edicts of the Ten Commandments. Then they compare the Confucian ideals they identify in the subsequent "The Wisdom of Confucius" worksheet with the Christian ideal.

The Wisdom of Confucius presents students with sayings of Confucius, from which students derive the essence of the qualities desired in Confucian and then Chinese civilization for many centuries thereafter. The Extra Challenge asks students to identify the differences between Jesus Christ and Confucius and their messages.

The Place of Women presents excerpts about women that express the role of women in Confucian and Buddhist societies. Students answer questions that help them understand the differences between the two. The Extra Challenge asks students to find passages from sacred texts of Vedic-Hindu religion, Judaism, and Christianity that similarly express the role and status of women and relate them to this discussion.

Religious and Ethical Beliefs reinforces students' understanding of ancient religious and ethical belief systems by naming characteristics of them and asking for identification by system.

Major Religions and Ethical Systems

c. 1000 B.C.E. to 300 C.E.

From very early times, people have held various forms of religious beliefs. They have had ideas about the origin of the world and the forces that control natural events. They have wondered about the possibility of life after death. Human beings in all parts of the world have developed concepts of many different deities (gods and goddesses). Each culture or area of the world tended to have its own belief system. In the era of early civilizations and empires, several major religions developed. They attracted thousands and, over time, millions of followers. They remain major world religions today.

Judaism

Judaism arose among the Hebrew (Jewish) people in very ancient times in the Middle East. The ancient Hebrews were nomadic herders. They worshipped Yahweh, a stern and angry god. This concept was well suited to the harsh, arid desert regions where the Hebrews lived. They believed they had a covenant, or pact, with Yahweh. They would worship Yahweh as the only god. In return, Yahweh would protect them as his "chosen people."

Over time, these nomadic herders became settled farmers and town dwellers. As their way of life changed, so did their concept of Yahweh. The Jews began to see Yahweh as the one god of all people. He demanded ethical behavior, as set forth in the Ten Commandments. Yet he also loved people and forgave those who were sorry for their sins.

Between about 720 and 585 B.C.E., conquering kingdoms forced the Jews out of their homelands in Israel and Judah. During their years of dispersal, the Jews developed an intricate code of laws. It governed almost every aspect of their lives. This, and their belief in a single protective god, gave the Jews a strong sense of community. The Jewish concern with ethical conduct and their belief in one god (called **monotheism**) had a great influence on later Western cultures.

(continued)

Major Religions and Ethical Systems (continued)

Hinduism

Hinduism developed in India. It had its roots in the Vedic religion of the Aryan people who moved into India around 1500 B.C.E. The religion got its name from its sacred writing, called Vedas. The Vedic religion was **polytheistic.** That is, it had many deities. Vedic priests carried out ritual sacrifices to these gods on behalf of the people. A key aspect of Vedic religion was **reincarnation.** This was a belief that after death a person's immortal essence was reborn in another living body. This new body could be animal or human. The form depended on the person's actions in the previous lives.

Connected with reincarnation was the Vedic concept of class and **caste.** According to Vedic belief, the creating god had divided human beings into four classes:

- Brahmans—priests, scholars
- Kshtriya—warriors, rulers, officials
- Vaisya—merchants, traders, land owners
- Shudra—peasants, laborers

and

- Untouchables—people outside of the class system

Within these classes were birth groups (*jati,* or castes). Each had its proper jobs and duties. Each person was born into a class and a caste. You lived your life only with other members of your class. Your goal was to fulfill all the duties of your existing class in this life-time. Only then could you hope to progress to a higher class and caste—in the next lifetime.

The Brahman class in Vedic society wielded great power. People of the lower classes resented this. They began to move Vedic religion into more equal and popular forms. By the fourth century C.E., Vedic religion had become Hinduism. Hinduism kept the Vedic belief in reincarnation and class/caste divisions. However, sacrifice became less important. Instead, people focused on individual, intense devotion to a chosen deity. Hinduism had, and has, a vast array of deities, and sects, and ways of worship. Together, all these deities are part of a unified whole. A single divine force unites the universe in the endless cycle of birth, death, and rebirth.

India was, and is, a land of vastly varied cultures and peoples. Hinduism, with its many deities and ways of worship, was easily absorbed into Indian society. It remains the religion of many millions of Indians, as well as other south Asians. (In this, it shares a place with Islam, which came to India in the 700s C.E.)

(continued)

Major Religions and Ethical Systems (continued)

Buddhism

Buddhism, like Hinduism, developed as a reaction against the Brahman priests and rigid class structure of Vedic times. Unlike Hinduism, Buddhism stemmed from a single person. He was Siddhartha Gautama, who lived from 563 to 483 B.C.E. He became known as the Buddha, the "Enlightened One." He was a wealthy young man who gave up his life of luxury at about age 30. He wandered for six years searching for spiritual insight. He wanted to find the cause and solution for human suffering. At last, one day while seated under a tree meditating, he had his revelation. He called what he saw the "Four Noble Truths":

- Truth One is that life is suffering; everyone suffers.

- Truth Two is that human desires cause suffering.

- Truth Three is that suffering ends when human beings stop desiring things, including individuality and happiness. This state in which all desires are erased is known as nirvana.

- Truth Four consists of the guidelines to reach nirvana, called the "Eightfold Path." Followers of this path would lead calm, peaceful, truthful, ethical lives on their journey toward nirvana.

Buddha then began preaching his message to the people. He and his followers practiced celibacy, poverty, and nonviolence. His disciples spread Buddhism throughout India and other parts of Asia.

Christianity

Christianity, like Buddhism, stemmed from one person. He was Jesus, a Jewish carpenter in Judaea (present-day Israel). Jesus objected to the Jewish religion as practiced during his time, around 30 C.E. He found it far too focused on worldly concerns and material things. He urged a return to the simple basic beliefs of Judaism, as set out in the Ten Commandments. To this, he added an overriding message of love. His god loved all people equally. This god did not favor priests or wealthy, upper-class people more than those who were poor and lower-class. People must mirror this godly love in their dealings with one another, he said. They must love others as they loved themselves; they must love even their enemies. "Do unto others as you would have others do unto you" is perhaps the best-known of Jesus' sayings.

(continued)

Major Religions and Ethical Systems *(continued)*

Some Jews saw Jesus as the Messiah, the savior foretold by the prophets. They hoped he had come to free them from Roman rule. This alarmed the Roman officials, who had Jesus condemned and put to death by crucifixion. Many of Jesus' followers believed he was the Son of God, Jesus Christ. God had sent this Messiah, they said, to show people the way to eternal life in heaven. They said the body of Christ had arisen from the tomb after his death. They spread this word and Christ's message among fellow Jews. Between 45 and 65 C.E., a Jewish convert to Christianity named Paul traveled widely. He spread the teachings of Jesus among non-Jewish people.

The new religion spread steadily. It appealed especially to the common people. Christians would not worship the Roman emperor as a god. At first, officials of the Roman Empire persecuted them because of this refusal. Christians lost their property and their lives. But then the Emperor Constantine became a Christian, soon after 300 C.E. He made Christianity a legal religion in the empire.

Confucianism

Confucianism is not a religion. Rather, it is an **ethical belief system.** It is a body of beliefs that govern human conduct, much as religions do. It was developed in China by the philosopher Kong Fu Zi (Master Kong), who lived from 551 to 479 B.C.E. He is best known in the West by the Latin form of his name, Confucius. He lived during a period of great disorder in China. In response, his teachings outline the way of life to follow in order to maintain a humane social order. Confucius taught that people should be unselfish, courteous, loyal, nonviolent, kind, helpful, fair, and honest. They should behave always with politeness and deference toward others, especially their parents and other family members. These ideals became a deeply ingrained part of Chinese culture in the years after the death of Confucius. Government officials, especially, were expected to follow the Confucian code of ethics and conduct.

Daoism

Daoism was a philosophy that developed into a religion. It was based on the teachings of Lao Tzu in the third century B.C.E. in China. Daoists sought to live in harmony with the eternal cycles and patterns of nature. This was not possible within the artificial bounds put on people by society. So Daoists turned away from the world, with its rules and rituals. They focused instead on individual thinking about dao, the way of nature. A humble, quiet, thoughtful, contented person was most likely to be in harmony with dao. Confucianism appealed to people who had some standing in higher society. Daoism, which scorned wealth and power, appealed to the common people. They added mystic beliefs about the spirit world to Daoism and turned it into a religion.

The Bhagavad Gita

The *Bhagavad Gita* is a portion of the great Hindu epic, the *Mahabharata*. In the Gita, the hero Arjuna speaks with the god Krishna, who appears in human form. Krishna expresses some basic aspects of Hindu religious beliefs and the way human life is to be conducted.

Directions: Read the excerpts and then answer the questions that follow.

The soul does not slay. The soul is not slain.
It is never born, nor does it ever die.
Having once been, it will never cease to be. . . .
Just as a man puts aside his worn-out clothes
And puts on others that are new,
So the soul lightly puts aside its worn-out body
And takes its place in one that is new. . . .
The end of birth is death, the end of death is birth.
This is ordained. Why would you grieve?

I created the four-caste system.
When the gods divided the primal person,
How many portions did they make?
What was his mouth, what were his arms?
What did they call his thighs and feet?
The Brahman was his mouth,
Of both his arms was the Kshatriya made.
His thighs became the Vaishya,
From his feet was born the Shudra. . . .
The actions of Brahmans, Kshatriyas and
    Vaishyas,
And Shudras, O slayer of thy foes,
Is fixed by the qualities of their own natures.

A Brahman's virtues, born of his nature,
Are serenity, self-control, austerity, purity,
Patience, uprightness, wisdom, and
    knowledge.
The actions of the Kshatriya, born of his nature,
Are valor, firmness, skill, spirit in battle,
Generosity, and a noble manner.
A Vaishya's task, born of his nature,
Is to till the ground, tend cattle, tend to trade.
A Shudra's state, born of his nature, is to serve.
A person who performs—contentedly,
    diligently—
The work allotted him, achieves perfection.

1. What basic Hindu belief does the first excerpt express? _____

    _____

2. What occupations or ranks of Hindu people would be members of the following classes?

    Brahmans _____

    Kshatriyas _____

    Vaisyas _____

    Shudras _____

77   *Focus on World History:*
The Era of Early Civilizations and Empires

The Buddhist Path

The Buddha outlined an "Eightfold Path" for believers to follow, as a guide to life. These are the guidelines a person must follow to attain nirvana, the state of nonbeing:

right understanding	right intention	right speech	right conduct
right livelihood	right effort	right mindfulness	right concentration

In practice, one set of Buddhist scriptures gives the following rules for lay people to follow. These rules are guides for staying on the Eightfold Path. (The top five are considered the most important.)

Abstain from destroying the life of any living thing.	Abstain from harsh or impolite talk.
Abstain from taking what is not given to you.	Abstain from frivolous or senseless talk.
Abstain from sexually immoral conduct.	Abstain from coveting other people's possessions.
Abstain from slander.	Abstain from ill will and hatred.
Abstain from false speech.	Abstain from heretical views.

Directions: On your own, or as a member of a small group, complete the following exercises.

1. Explain how each of the "Abstain from" rules applies to one or more steps on the Eightfold Path.

   _____

   _____

   _____

   _____

   _____

2. Identify a person—contemporary or historical—who, in your opinion, followed closely the Buddha's Eightfold Path in her or his life. Relate specific actions, words, and/or teachings of that person to steps on the Path and/or to the "Abstain from" rules of conduct.

   _____

   _____

   _____

   _____

   _____

The Ten Commandments

According to the Judaic Torah, the Hebrew leader Moses received tablets from the Hebrew god, Yahweh. These tablets recorded ten rules for right living by faithful Jews. These are known as the Ten Commandments. They are:

1. I am the Lord, your God. You shall have no other gods before me.

2. You shall not make any graven images [idols]; you shall not bow down before them or worship them.

3. You shall not take the name of the Lord, your God, in vain.

4. Remember to keep holy the Sabbath.

5. Honor your father and your mother.

6. You shall not kill.

7. You shall not commit adultery.

8. You shall not steal.

9. You shall not bear false witness against your neighbors.

10. You shall not covet your neighbor's house, you shall not covet your neighbor's wife, nor his male or female slave, nor his ox or ass, nor anything else that belongs to your neighbor.

Directions: Compare these Hebrew Ten Commandments with the Buddhist Eightfold Path and the ten Buddhist guidelines for right conduct. What rules/guidelines are the same or similar? What rules/guidelines are not shared?

Extra Challenge: Do this Extra Challenge after you have completed three other worksheets: "The Buddhist Path," "The Christian Ideal," and "The Wisdom of Confucius." Role-play a discussion among Jesus Christ, the Buddha, Confucius, and Moses (as the representative of Yahweh). In your chosen or assigned role, talk about the standards for human behavior that you call for and the rewards and punishments for that behavior.

---

79   *Focus on World History:*
The Era of Early Civilizations and Empires

The Christian Ideal

Directions: The New Testament of the Bible is a sacred text of Christians. It relates what habits of life that Jesus Christ taught would bring blessings from God. You can read some of them below. Then read the statements in the box and answer the questions that follow.

Blessed are the poor in spirit, for theirs is the kingdom of heaven.

Blessed are the meek, for they shall possess the earth.

Blessed are they who mourn, for they shall be comforted.

Blessed are they who hunger and thirst for justice, for they shall be satisfied.

Blessed are the merciful, for they shall obtain mercy.

Blessed are the clean of heart, for they shall see God.

Blessed are the peacemakers, for they shall be called children of God.

You have heard that it was said to the ancients, "You shall not kill," and that whoever shall kill shall be liable to judgment. But I say to you that everyone who is angry with his brother shall be liable to judgment.

You have heard that it was said to the ancients, "You shall not commit adultery." But I say to you that anyone who so much as looks with lust at a woman has already committed adultery with her in his heart.

Again, you have heard that it was said to the ancients, "You shall not swear falsely, but fulfill your oaths to the Lord." But I say to you not to swear at all. . . . But let your speech be, "Yes, yes." "No, no."

You have heard that it was said, "An eye for an eye," and "A tooth for a tooth." But I say to you not to resist the evildoer; on the contrary, if someone strike thee on the right cheek, turn to him the other also.

You have heard that it was said, "You shall love your neighbor and shall hate your enemy." But I say to you, love your enemies, do good to those who hate you, and pray for those who persecute and calumniate* you.

* make false statements about

---

1. Does Jesus Christ alter or add to the Ten Commandments in these sayings? If so, in what ways?

   _____

   _____

2. After completing Worksheet 5: Which of the qualities that you list on the Confucius

   worksheet would also apply to the Christian ideal? _____

   _____

The Wisdom of Confucius

Confucius, the great philosopher of China, developed a moral system to guide people in the good way of life. Here are some of his guidelines for good conduct.

If leaders love courtesy, their people will not dare to be disrespectful. If leaders love justice, people will not dare to be unruly. If leaders love trustworthiness, people will not dare to be dishonest.

Be sedate and serious at home, attentive at work, strictly sincere in human relations. Even if you travel among uncivilized people, you must not neglect these virtues.

Superior people understand matters of justice. Petty people understand matters of profit.

You have perfect virtue if you can practice five things in the world: respectfulness, generosity, truthfulness, earnestness, and kindness. If you are respectful, you will not be treated with disrespect. If you are generous, you will win people. If you are truthful, you will be trusted. If you are earnest, you will be successful. If you are kind, you will be able to employ the services of others.

If your personal conduct is correct, things get done without any orders being issued. If your personal conduct is not correct, no one will obey even if you do give orders.

To hear a lot, choose what is good, and follow it. To see a lot and remember it: this is next to knowledge.

When you do things for your parents, you may object, but gently. If you see that they are not inclined to take your advice, then respect them and do not oppose them. Should they punish you, do not protest.

What I don't want others to do to me, I also do not want to do to others.

Even if you have fine abilities, if you are arrogant and stingy, those abilities are not worth considering.

Superior people are even-tempered and satisfied. Petty people are always full of distress.

Place loyalty and faithfulness first. Don't associate with anyone who is not as good as you are, and don't hesitate to change when you have made a mistake.

(continued)

The Wisdom of Confucius *(continued)*

Do not regard what is not courteous. Do not listen to what is not courteous. Do not say what is not courteous. Do not do what is not courteous. This is perfect virtue.

A youth should be dutiful at home, respectful to elders in public; be earnest and trustworthy, love everyone, and cultivate the friendship of good people.

Promote the honest and set aside the crooked, and the people will obey. Promote the crooked and set aside the honest, and the people will not obey.

Don't talk about things that are already done; don't protest about things that are already over; don't criticize what has already happened.

When you see wise people, think of becoming equal to them. When you see unwise people, reflect inwardly on yourself.

Virtuous people do not contend over anything.

Directions: From what you have read, make a list below of the most important qualities a person should have and should live his or her life by, according to Confucius.

_____

_____

_____

_____

_____

_____

_____

_____

_____

Extra Challenge: In chart form, summarize the differences between Jesus Christ and Confucius and their messages.

The Place of Women

Directions: What was the role of women within the religious and ethical systems of the ancient world? Here are some examples. Read the excerpts and answer the questions that follow.

Mengzi, Confucian philosopher

A woman's duties are to cook the five grains, heat the wine, look after her parents-in-law, make clothes, and that is all! She has no ambition to manage affairs outside the house. She must follow the "three submissions": When she is young, she must submit to her parents. When she is married, she must submit to her husband. When she is widowed, she must submit to her son.

Buddhist sacred text

In five ways should a wife be ministered to by her husband: by respect, by courtesy, by faithfulness, by handing over authority to her, by providing her with adornment.

In these five ways does the wife, ministered to by her husband, love him: by performing her duties well, by hospitality to the kin of both, by faithfulness, by watching over the goods he brings, and by skill and industry in discharging all her business.

1. What differences do these passages suggest in the role of women in Buddhist India and China and in Confucian China?

    _____

    _____

    _____

2. Do you think men's and women's real lives ran along the lines outlined by the Buddhist text and Mengzi? For example, how might women of the lower classes have been affected to a greater or lesser degree than upper-class women by either of these models for women's roles and status?

    _____

    _____

    _____

Extra Challenge: Find passages from the sacred texts of Vedic-Hindu religion, Judaism, and Christianity that express the preferred role/status of women in those religions and ways of life. Discuss by extending these additional passages to the above questions. You could summarize your findings in chart form. Or you could role-play a discussion among women of these different cultures. Or you could write a "day in the life" sketch of a woman in each culture.

Religious and Ethical Beliefs

Directions: Given below are various ethical beliefs and forms of religious expression. Label each with the religion or ethical system(s) that it is part of. Use the letters of the religious/ethical system(s) listed in the box below. (You will use more than one letter for many items.)

Vedic religion (V)	Christianity (Chr)	Judaism (J)	Buddhism (B)
Hinduism (H)	Confucianism (Cf)	Daoism (D)	traditional Chinese religion (Ch)

1. recognizes powerful, divine forces of nature: _____

2. has many shrines to various deities across the country: _____

3. is most popular with common people, not upper classes: _____

4. has priests to conduct proper rituals: _____

5. preaches nonviolence: _____

6. has sacred texts: _____

7. has monks and nuns: _____

8. has only one god: _____

9. has female deities: _____

10. denies the importance of deities: _____

11. harmonizes with patterns and cycles of natural world: _____

12. practices sacrifice of animals: _____

13. stresses solitary contemplation and meditation: _____

14. sometimes builds elaborate temples or churches: _____

15. believes in survival after death in some form: _____

16. stresses courtesy, loyalty, and deference toward others: _____

17. assigns specific roles to specific classes of people in life: _____

18. calls for ancestor veneration: _____

Great Empires

The objectives of this unit are to help students understand how large-scale empires arose in the Mediterranean basin, China, and India in the years from 500 B.C.E. to 300 C.E., and to learn about the characteristics of those empires. The empires of Rome, Han China, and Maurya India united areas that were very diverse both geographically and ethnically. Holding these areas together required a strong, efficient central government backed by a large, effective army. Frontier defense units protected the empires' borders, while a network of roads, widespread trade, and provincial imperial centers diffused each ruling center's culture throughout the empire.

Rome began as a republic but became an empire as the territory under its control kept expanding. China's first empires were relatively compact, but under the Han dynasty, the empire expanded to include most of China. Unlike Rome, China remained under the rule of emperors until modern times. India's first Maurya ruler was very autocratic, but his Buddhist grandson ruled benevolently. Eventually, each of these empires crumbled under the pressures of high taxes needed to pay the expenses of administration and defense and of opposition along the borders and internally among restless ethnic groups. This unit's activities are designed to draw students into a better understanding of these large empires.

Student Activities

Slavery in the Ancient World puts students into the place of slaves in four different ancient societies. Students describe the conditions of their life in each society and then role-play a conversation among those slaves, or between one of those slaves and her or his mistress or master.

War Technology 2 takes a second look at technologies of war, in this case those that helped Greece, Macedonia, and China expand (also Rome, by borrowing some of these technologies). Students identify the society that produced the trireme, phalanx, catapult, and crossbow and explain what advantage each of these gave in warfare.

Mapping the Chinese Empire uses mapping to make students familiar with the many different geographic regions and features of China. Related questions in the answer section extend students' understanding of this topic.

The Life of Chinese Peasants presents the lyrics of an ancient Zhou dynasty song about the daily lives of Chinese peasants across the changing seasons. Students apply the information in the song by comparing the life of rural Chinese peasants with other classes of people in Han society, using one of several suggested comparison techniques.

The Mandate of Heaven presents an explanation of the Mandate from the ancient *Book of History*, which students use to analyze the Mandate and the reasons why Chinese rulers adopted it.

Mapping the Indian Empire uses mapping to make students familiar with the many different geographic regions and features of India. Related questions in the answer section extend students' understanding of this topic.

Women in India presents excerpts from Maurya Indian laws relating to women, which students interpret to gain a better understanding of the status of women in this society. Students follow up by comparing women's status in other ancient societies.

Women Rule in Egypt presents an inscription of Hatshepsut and a description of Cleopatra written by Plutarch, which serve as springboards for student research on the ways in which these two Egyptian rulers acquired and used power, and for what ends.

Greek and Roman Architecture: A Local Hunt shows students examples of Greek and Roman architecture and demonstrates the lasting use of these styles by having students search their local area to find examples of Greek- and Roman-style buildings.

An Empire Falls presents a vivid eyewitness account of the battle of Adrianople, where the mighty Roman army fell to the Visigoths. Students write their own vivid firsthand account of a battle scene they view on video. This battle narrative can also serve as a springboard for discussion about the reasons for the decline and fall of the Roman Empire and a comparison with reasons why other empires of ancient times fell.

The Empires of Rome and Han China provides a framework in which students can identify the many similarities as well as the differences between these two empires.

Great Empires

c. 500 B.C.E. to 300 C.E.

In the years from 500 B.C.E. to 300 C.E., three large-scale empires arose. They formed in the Mediterranean area, China, and India. The world had seen empires before, such as the Assyrian and Babylonian ones. The empire of Alexander the Great had been very large, but short-lived. Now, the empires of Rome and Han China created even larger multiethnic empires. The Roman Empire drew the Eurasian and African worlds much closer together. The Han Empire did the same for the East and Southeast Asian worlds. At about the same time, the Maurya Empire united much of India.

The Roman Empire

The city of Rome was founded in about 750 B.C.E. It sits on seven hills in the midpoint of the Italian peninsula. The peninsula itself is a midpoint of the Mediterranean Sea. With the island of Sicily, Italy nearly reaches across the Mediterranean to Africa. This central location helped Rome develop into a powerful empire.

> According to legend, Rome was founded by Romulus, an abandoned baby who had been nursed by a mother wolf.

The early Romans set up a republic. In this type of government, power rests with the citizens who are entitled to vote. At first, Roman government was fairly democratic. But over time, class divisions sharpened. The republic then was run by upper-class men, called patricians. They made policy and governed through the Senate, whose membership they chose. Other Romans, called plebeians, did have some voting and lawmaking rights. Two consuls were elected for one-year terms. They acted as the chief magistrates (judges) and army commanders.

By the 200s B.C.E., Rome had taken control of almost all of the Italian peninsula. Then it began to expand beyond its borders. Soon it controlled the entire Mediterranean area.

As Rome's empire expanded, its economy changed. Imported grains wiped out many small farmers. They moved to the cities. There, with no jobs, they depended on the government for food. Wealthy people became richer, using slave labor to work their huge estates. Soldiers gave their loyalty to the commanders who paid them. Political control came into the hands of military leaders. They used their armies to conquer new lands. Then they used their military fame and power to become rulers of Rome. Julius Caesar became dictator of Rome in 49 B.C.E. He was murdered in 44 B.C.E. His successor, Octavian, became the first emperor of Rome.

> During the 300s C.E., Rome had 175 public holidays a year.

(continued)

Great Empires (continued)

By 120 C.E., Rome ruled a vast empire in Europe, southwest Asia, and North Africa. It maintained its control through a fine system of roads, a uniform set of laws, and good administration. Army units lived along the frontiers to keep the borders secure. People who lived in the provinces were made Roman citizens. Cities in the provinces were rebuilt on the pattern of Rome. All this produced a united and cohesive empire.

> The Roman Empire enjoyed a long period of peace from 27 B.C.E. to 180 C.E. It is called the *Pax Romana*, the "Roman Peace."

Han China

In 1027 B.C.E., the Zhou line of Chinese rulers took over from the Shang. The Zhou rulers claimed they had a "Mandate of Heaven" to rule. They said the gods would back them as long as they were fair and honest rulers. Zhou rule continued until 221 B.C.E. There was no strong central government. This led, late in the Zhou era, to much warring between rival city-states.

> The word *Qin* is probably the origin of the Western name *China*.

The Shang and Zhou both ruled over a fairly small area of China. In 221 B.C.E. Shi Huangdi founded China's first empire, the Qin. But the Han dynasty soon took over. The Han ruled a greatly expanded empire for 400 years, from 206 B.C.E. to 220 C.E. Over time, the Han Chinese took control of areas where other **ethnic** groups lived. They ruled over regions that were very diverse in geography, climate,

and cultures. The Han used an imperial system much like that of Rome. They set uniform standards for things such as writing, measurement, and coins. They built many roads and cities like Chang'an, the capital. As in the Roman Empire, the Han united its varied peoples in a common culture.

During the Zhou and Han periods, many lasting aspects of Chinese life took shape. The philosopher Confucius laid down the basic precepts for living a good life and governing well. To become a Chinese civil servant, a person had to pass a test on classic literature and law. Obeying the family and the state was very important.

Unlike Rome, China remained a unified empire for over 2,000 years. Dynasties changed, but the rule of emperors endured until the twentieth century.

(continued)

Great Empires *(continued)*

The Bases and the Declines of Rome and China

The family was the basic unit of society in both Rome and Han China. It included people in all living generations of the family. The father ruled this unit absolutely. All members had a duty to obey the family and be loyal to it in all things. People felt that they had the same duty to obey and be loyal to the state. This created a very strong and stable society.

Another foundation of the Roman and Han states was their citizen-farmers. Farming was the economic base of each state. Farmers paid a portion of their crops to the state in taxes. The farmers also provided manpower for public works projects and for the army.

> Both Rome and China built walls to protect their frontiers. Hadrian's Wall kept Scottish Picts out of Britain. The Great Wall stopped nomads of central Asia from raids into China.

Reasons for decline were similar for both empires. Wealthy landowners lost power to the emperors at first. But then they began to take back control of vast tracts of land. The peasants became tenant farmers, tied to the landowner rather than the state. The huge expense of frontier defense chipped away at the empires' economic bases. As the empires became weaker, the opposing people on the frontier borders took notice. In time, they were able to invade and destroy the empires.

The Great Wall of China

Mauryan India

India also was ruled by an empire during part of this period. In 321 B.C.E. Chandragupta Maurya became ruler of the eastern Indian kingdom of Magadha. He soon extended his rule to central, northern, and western India. This was the first time such a large part of India had been under a central rule.

Setting up a central rule was no more easy in India than in China, or Rome. Like China, India is a land of many different geographic regions. It also has a vast array of ethnic groups, languages, and customs. In spite of this, Chandragupta and the rulers who came after him were able to keep order. This first emperor was very autocratic—that is, he had total power and ruled as he pleased. He divided the empire into local units along traditional boundaries. He kept a large army, set high taxes, and controlled major industries.

(continued)

Great Empires *(continued)*

Ashoka was Chandragupta's grandson. He ruled from 269 to 232 B.C.E. He used the army to expand the empire farther. One campaign was so bloody and brutal, the young king became disgusted. He converted to Buddhism and changed to a kinder, gentler form of rule. By example, he urged his people to be pious and to love and be tolerant of one another. He showed them how to hold to duty and honor in their lives. Ashoka had his sayings about how to behave carved on rock pillars all through the empire. He sent missionaries far afield to spread the message of Buddhism. Many of his subjects admired Ashoka and adopted Buddhism and Ashoka's ways themselves.

The Mauryan Empire lasted for a while after Ashoka's death, but not for long. It broke up in 184 B.C.E. India wasn't united under a single rule again until the Gupta Empire in the fourth century C.E.

Bullock cart—India

Focus on World History:
The Era of Early Civilizations and Empires

Slavery in the Ancient World

Directions: Slavery was an ever-present element of ancient societies. But the conditions of slavery varied from society to society. In the spaces below, put yourself in the place of a slave in each named society. Describe the conditions of your life.

1. You are a slave in Han China. _____

   _____

   _____

   _____

2. You are a slave in Mauryan India. _____

   _____

   _____

   _____

3. You are a slave in classical-era Greece. _____

   _____

   _____

   _____

4. You are a slave in imperial Rome. _____

   _____

   _____

   _____

Further Directions: Now, with classmates, role-play a conversation among slaves in the four different societies about their status and their feelings about their lives. Or role-play a dialogue between a slave and her or his mistress or master, in which the slave argues for her or his freedom or more privileges.

War Technology 2

Warfare was a major element in expanding a state's area of control and in establishing empires. These world-affecting changes were helped along a lot by ever-improving war technologies. Each society had its own particular improvements.

Directions: Tell what nation/empire first developed each war-related technology shown below, and explain what advantage it gave in warfare.

1. Trireme

   Origin: _____

   Advantage: _____

2. Phalanx

   Origin: _____

   Advantage: _____

3. Catapult

   Origin: _____

   Advantage: _____

4. Crossbow

   Origin: _____

   Advantage: _____

Mapping the Chinese Empire

Directions: China is a vast land with many different geographic regions. On your map of China, locate and label the items listed below. Use different-colored pencils to indicate the different land areas: mountains, river floodplains, arid plateau, steppe, desert.

Mountains	Bodies of Water	Regions	Cities
Himalayas	Pacific Ocean	Takla Makan Desert	Anyang
Kunlun	Yellow Sea	Gobi Desert	Chang'an (Xi'an)
Tien Shan	South China Sea	Mongolian Steppe	Luoyang
Altai	Yangzi River	Tibetan Plateau	Zhengzhou
	Huang He (Yellow) River		
	Xi River		

Also, outline the Han Empire.

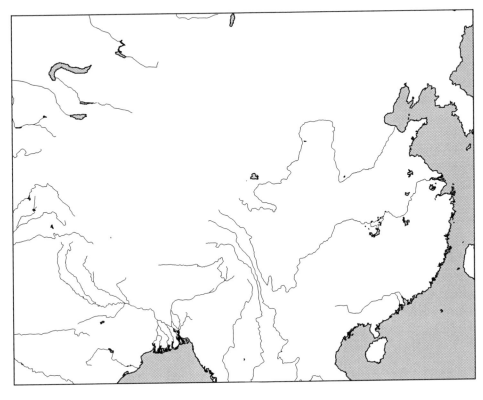

Focus on World History:
The Era of Early Civilizations and Empires

The Life of Chinese Peasants

The ancient written and artistic records don't tell us a lot about the lives of common people. A song of the Zhou dynasty of the eighth century B.C.E., however, gives us a picture of the lives of Chinese peasants:

In the days of the first month the wind blows cold.
In the days of the second month, the air is shivering cold.
Without coats, without wool garments,
How could we last to the end of the year?
In the days of the third month we take up our plows;
In the days of the fourth we step out to the fields
Along with wives and children.
We bring our food hampers to the
    southern acres.
When the spring days become warm
And the oriole sings,
The girls carry their deep baskets
And make their way along the narrow
    paths,
Looking for the tender mulberry leaves. . . .
A girl's heart is wounded with sadness.
For she fears she must go with one of the
    young lords. . . .
In the tenth month the cricket
Goes under our beds.
We fill up the chinks in the walls to smoke out the rats;
We stop up the north-facing windows and seal the doors.
Come, wife and children.
The change of the year is at hand.
Let us live inside the house.

Directions: Compare the life of rural peasants with other members of Han society: an urban common person, a merchant, an urban slave, a government official, a member of the royal household, a country landowner, a married woman of any class, and so on. You could write a poem or song like the one above describing the life of one type of person. You could write brief biographical sketches of different Chinese people (give each one an individual name). You could role-play part of a person's or family's daily routine. Or you could write a series of journal entries, imagining yourself to be a particular person in Han China—for example, the girl in the song above whose "heart is wounded with sadness."

The Mandate of Heaven

Chinese rulers derived their authority to rule from the "Mandate of Heaven." The excerpt below is from the ancient *Book of History*, or *Shu Ching*. In it, the king's chief minister, I Yin, instructs the new young king on how to be a good ruler and maintain the Mandate of Heaven.

Directions: Read the excerpt and then answer the questions that follow.

> In the twelfth month of the first year . . . I Yin made sacrifices to the former king, and presented the heir-king reverently before the shrine of his grandfather. . . . I Yin then clearly described all the virtues of the Meritorious Ancestor [the Shang dynasty founder] as instruction for the young king.
>
> He said, "Oh! in olden times the former kings of Xia earnestly cultivated their virtue, and then Heaven sent no disasters. The spirits of the hills and rivers were tranquil; and the birds and beasts, the fishes and tortoises, all enjoyed their lives according to their nature. But the descendants of these kings did not follow their example, and great Heaven sent down disasters, using our ruler [T'ang, the first Shang ruler], whom Heaven favored as its agent.
>
> "Our king of Shang brilliantly displayed his sagely prowess. In place of oppression he ruled with generous gentleness, and millions of the people gave him their hearts. . . . He extensively sought out wise men, who should be helpful to you, his descendant and heir. He laid down the punishments for officers, and warned those who were in authority [about evil ways]. . . .
>
> "Oh! do you, who now succeed to the throne, revere these warnings in your person. Think of them! sacred counsels of vast importance, admirable words set forth with force! The ways of Heaven are certain: On the person who does good it sends down all blessings, and on the evil-doer it sends down all miseries. If you are virtuous, whether in small things or in large, the myriad regions of the empire will have cause for rejoicing. If you are not virtuous, whether in large things or in small, this will bring the ruin of your ancestral temple."

1. How does this excerpt express the "Mandate of Heaven"? Explain the Mandate in your own words.

   _____

   _____

2. This document was written during the time of the Zhou dynasty. Why was the Mandate of Heaven important to the Zhou (they may, in fact, have invented it)?

   _____

   _____

   _____

Mapping the Indian Empire

Directions: India is a vast and diverse land with many different geographic regions. On this map of India, locate and label the items listed below. Use different-colored pencils to indicate the different land areas: mountains, river floodplains, arid plateau, tropical coastal strip, desert.

Mountains	Bodies of Water	Regions	Cities
Himalayas	Arabian Sea	Kashmir	Delhi
Hindu Kush	Bay of Bengal	Punjab	Ayodhya
Vindhya	Indian Ocean	Bengal	Pataliputra
Khyber Pass	Ganges River	Sri Lanka	
	Indus River	Thar Desert	
Also, outline the area of the Mauryan Empire.		Deccan Plateau	

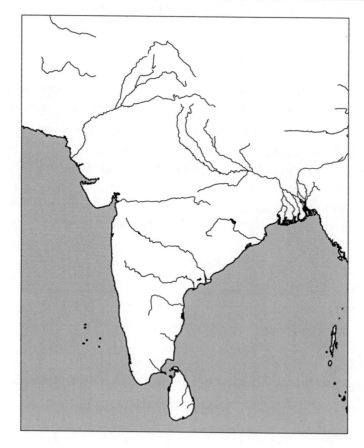

96   *Focus on World History:*
                                                                  The Era of Early Civilizations and Empires

Women in India

Kautilya was an older advisor to Chandragupta Maurya, the young ruler of the Mauryan Empire. His advice on laws and how to govern are collected in a text called the *Arthashastra*. Here are some excerpts from that text that give us some idea of the status of women in Mauryan India.

Directions: Read the excerpts below and then answer the questions that follow.

Jewelry or means of support make up the property of a woman. Means of support above two thousand shall be endowed in her name. There is no limit to jewelry. The wife may use this property to maintain her son, her daughter-in-law, or herself, whenever her husband is absent and has made no provision for her support.

When a woman's husband dies, and she resolves to remain a widow, she shall immediately be given back her endowment and her jewelry, plus the balance of the marriage-price due her. If after she gets these things back, she remarries, she must pay them back, plus interest.

If a wife gives birth to no live children, or has no male children, or is barren, her husband shall wait for eight years before marrying someone else. If a wife gives birth only to a dead child, the husband must wait for ten years before marrying someone else. If a wife gives birth only to females, the husband has to wait for twelve years before marrying someone else.

If a husband has a bad character, or is gone far away for a long time, or is disloyal to his ruler, or is likely to put his wife's life in danger, or has fallen from his caste, or has lost his virility, his wife may leave him.

A woman who hates her husband cannot divorce her husband against his will. Nor can a man divorce his wife against her will. But if both husband and wife hate each other, they may by mutual consent divorce.

Unruly women shall not be struck more than three times, on the hips, with a bamboo stick, a rope, or the palm of the hand.

What do these excerpts tell us about the status of women in India during the Mauryan Empire? Do these rules seem harsh to you, or reasonable? How does the status of Indian women seem to compare with the status of women in China? in Rome? in ancient Greece?

Focus on World History:
The Era of Early Civilizations and Empires

Women Rule in Egypt

Most of Egypt's rulers were men. But Egypt did have some notable female rulers. Hatshepsut and Cleopatra were among them. Hatshepsut was a native Egyptian. Cleopatra was one of the Greek Ptolemy rulers of the Egyptian Roman empire period. They acquired power in different ways, both to promote the national interests of Egypt. Contrast these two descriptions, one dictated by Hatshepsut and the other written by Plutarch, a male Greek historian.

Hatshepsut, pharaoh of Egypt, c. 1460 B.C.E.

Hear ye, all people, I have done these things as my heart dictated. I have restored what had been ruined. I have raised up what had crumbled since the Hyksos were in the midst of us, and the vagabonds were in the midst of them. They ruled without Re. Now I am established upon the thrones of Re. I was foretold to be a born conqueror. I am come as the serpent of Horus, flaming against my enemies. I have driven off those whom the gods hate, and earth has erased their footprints. This is the commandment of Re, the father of my fathers, and I shall not allow damage to what Amon has commanded to be whole. My own rule endures like the mountains, and the sun disc shines out and spreads its rays over my royalty. My falcon flies above my emblem for all of eternity.

Cleopatra, queen of Egypt (69–30 B.C.E.)

Now Cleopatra's actual beauty, they said, was not in itself so remarkable that no one could be compared with her, or that no one could see her without being struck by it. Rather, the contact of her presence, if you lived with her, was irresistible. The attraction of her person, joining with the charm of her conversation, and the character that attended all she said or did, was something bewitching. It was a pleasure merely to hear the sound of her voice, with which, like an instrument of many strings, she could pass from one language to another. . . . Antony was so captivated by her that he allowed himself to be carried away by her to Alexandria. . . . Cleopatra, by exercising her flattery . . . in many ways, and by constantly introducing some fresh pleasure and charm into Antony's days, whether serious or mirthful, got him completely under her sway.

Directions: Research the ways in which Hatshepsut and Cleopatra acquired power and used it. Consider these questions: Hatshepsut's inscription makes her sound mighty and all-powerful. Is this an exaggeration? How did artworks depict Hatshepsut? Why? What other Roman ruler did Cleopatra forge a relationship with? What advantages did Cleopatra's strategy bring to herself and to Egypt? How did Cleopatra's rule end?

Focus on World History:
The Era of Early Civilizations and Empires

Greek and Roman Architecture: A Local Hunt

Shown below are two public buildings, one from ancient Greece and another from ancient Rome. Each shows typical elements of Greek and Roman public buildings. Greek public buildings are rectangular, balanced with dignified columns topped by flat beams and decorated with carvings. Roman buildings are similar, but they add the arch and domed spaces.

The Parthenon (Greece)

Roman column

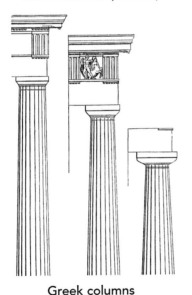

Greek columns

The Coliseum (Rome)

Directions: Search your local area to find examples of Greek-style and Roman-style public buildings. Take photos to display in class. What elements of the Greek and Roman architectural styles do you see in your buildings? When was this a popular style for new buildings in the United States?

Focus on World History:
The Era of Early Civilizations and Empires

An Empire Falls

In 378 C.E., the Visigoths who had settled along the Rhine-Danube frontier of the Roman Empire rebelled against the Romans. The Visigoths and the Romans fought at Adrianople. The decisive victory by the Visigoths foretold the fall of the mighty Roman Empire soon after, in the early 400s. A Greek historian and journalist named Ammianus penned a vivid account of this great battle.

Soon our infantry too was left unsupported. The companies and regiments were shoved together so closely that a soldier could scarcely draw his sword, or even withdraw his hand after he had once stretched it out.

By this time such great clouds of dust arose that it was hardly possible to see the sky. The air resounded with terrible cries. The darts, which brought death on every side, reached their mark and fell with deadly effect, for no one could see them quickly enough to place himself on guard. The barbarians, rushing on with their enormous army, beat down our horses and men and gave us no open spaces where we could fall back to operate. They were so closely packed that it became impossible for us to escape by forcing a path through them. Our men finally began to despise the thought of death and again taking their swords slew all they encountered. Helmets and breastplates were smashed in pieces by mutual blows of battle-axes.

Then you might see the barbarian, towering in his fierceness, hissing or shouting, fall with his legs pierced through, or his right hand cut off, sword and all, or his side transfixed, and still, in the last gasp of life, casting around his defiant glances.

The plain was covered with corpses, showing the mutual ruin of the combatants. The groans of the dying, or of men horribly wounded, were intense and caused much dismay on all sides. Amidst all this great tumult and confusion, our infantry were exhausted by toil and danger, until at last they had neither the strength left to fight nor the spirit to plan anything. . . .

The sun, now high in the heavens, scorched the Romans, who were emaciated by hunger, worn out with battle, and scarcely able to bear the weight of their own weapons. At last our columns were entirely beaten back by the overpowering weight of the barbarians. They took to disorderly flight—the only resource under the circumstances—each man seeking to save himself as best he could.

Scarcely one third of the entire army escaped. Never . . . had there been so destructive a slaughter recorded in our annals.

Directions: Watch a battle scene—an ancient one, if possible—in a video. Then write your own vivid firsthand account of the battle.

Focus on World History:
The Era of Early Civilizations and Empires

The Empires of Rome and Han China

Directions: The empires of Rome and Han China had many similarities. They had important differences, too. Fill in the chart below and on the next page to summarize those similarities and differences.

	Han China	Rome
Size of empire		
Basic economic activity to support empire		
Changes in land ownership		
Techniques of imperial government		
Defense of frontiers		
Effect on subject peoples		

(continued)

The Empires of Rome and Han China *(continued)*

	Han China	Rome
Trade networks		
Position of the family		
Position of the emperor and justification of emperor's rule		
Economic/social mobility and place of the individual		
Long-term continuity of imperial tradition		
Effects of a new religion on the empire		
General religious beliefs		

ANSWERS, ADDITIONAL ACTIVITIES, AND ASSESSMENTS

Unit 1: Early Humans

Worksheet 1: Human Beings Emerge (page 6)

Australopithecus afarensis—eastern and southern Africa, c. 4 million years ago; small brain (size of modern ape), walked upright, used natural objects as simple tools.

Homo habilis—eastern and southern Africa, c. 2–3 million years ago; four feet tall; small brain was nonetheless 50% larger than that of *A. afarensis;* made simple stone tools, lived in nuclear families.

Homo erectus—appeared in Africa c. 1.6 million years ago, first human to be found outside Africa, found widely in Asia, Africa, and Europe by 500,000 years ago; used fire, hunted large animals, made and used hand-axes and chopping tools, had larger brain capacity than *H. habilis,* had apelike facial features, may have had primitive speech.

Homo sapiens—Africa, Asia, Europe 400,000 to 100,000 years ago; brain one-third larger than that of *H. erectus,* great speech capacity, more sophisticated hand tools.

Homo sapiens sapiens—emerged approximately 35,000 to 40,000 years ago in Africa, Asia, Europe; no apelike facial features; had elaborate speech patterns and enhanced mastery of fire; made specialized tools of varied materials including tool-making tools, made more advanced weapons such as the bow and arrow and spear-thrower and harpoon, made dugout canoes, domesticated the dog and the goat.

Worksheet 2: Human Beings Spread Across the World (page 7)

You could assign the site location mapping task, or parts of it, to groups of students working cooperatively.

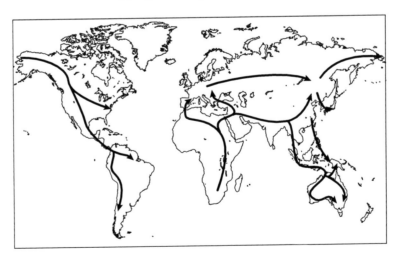

103

Worksheet 3: Stone Age Tools (page 8)

Tools shown: axe (chopping stone attached to handle), spear, knives in sheaths, bows and arrows

Hominid or human type: *Homo sapiens*

Evidence: Only *Homo sapiens* had a large enough brain to hunt large animals successfully and to make tools of combined materials like bows and arrows, spears, and axes with handles.

Worksheet 4: Elements of Stone Age Life (page 9)

You can make completion of this worksheet into a valuable comparison exercise by assigning various students or pairs of students to report on different Stone Age groups in different locations around the world—for example, northern Europe/Russia, North Africa, East Africa, South Africa, China, Java, Australia, northwestern North America, eastern North America, South America (Chile or Brazil), Middle East. Students would then compare their responses for each element of the worksheet in a class discussion.

Worksheet 5: Ötzi the Ice Man (page 10)

Students can use the following site to research this subject:

The Iceman—"Man from the Hauslabjoch" http://info.uibk.ac.at/c/c5/c552/Forschung/ Iceman/iceman-en.html

1. clothing—fur hat and shoes, deerskin vest, leather leggings, woven grass shawl
2. hunting items—long bow, arrows, flint points
3. tools—copper-headed axe, flint knife, flint scraper, flint awl, fire-starting tools, animal sinew, pointed bone tool
4. medical supplies—two tree fungi
5. containers—quiver for arrows, sheath for knife, birchbark cup, backpack

Worksheet 6: Discoverers of Prehistory (page 11)

1. A geologist searches for and studies rock formations and other earth evidence to reconstruct landscapes; a geologist analyzes fossilized rocks to determine age of fossils in them.

2. An archaeologist searches for and studies created human remains, such as stone tools and buildings, to learn about human societies and cultures.

3. A paleontologist searches for and studies animal fossils, and interprets them to identify possible prehistory climates and environments.

4. A paleoanthropologist searches for and studies hominid and early human remains in order to learn about the biology and physical appearance of early people.

Worksheet 7: Ongoing Discoveries (page 12)

Use the readings on the activity sheet as a springboard for an ongoing class project. Direct students to keep track of new findings in archaeology and paleoanthropology. Tell them to check newspapers and newsmagazines, television, and the Internet, and to look through journals like *Science* and *Archaeology*. Keep a class display or file of any new findings. Do they change any information or dates in your textbook or in this book?

Additional Activity Suggestions

You could have the students do any of the following activities.

1. Create a poster showing the various types of Stone Age dwelling places, including pits in the ground, dry riverbeds, overhanging rock shelters, caves, windbreaks of brush, and various types of huts.

2. Bring to class pictures comparing different skeletons and skulls of different types of early hominids and humans. Point out the differences.

3. As a class project, collect the creation myths of a number of different world cultures. What does each myth tell about the values and beliefs of the culture that invented it? Why do most cultures have a creation myth?

4. Research and report on one hunter-gatherer, Stone-Age-type society that has existed and been studied in modern times.

5. Research and report on the extinction of large mammals in different parts of the earth during prehistory. Come to a reasoned conclusion about which possible cause (environmental calamity, disease, climate change, human hunt-

ing, and so on) is most likely to have caused these extinctions. You could also create a poster illustrating these animals (and showing their size in relation to humans), especially the unfamiliar and exotic large extinct animals of Australia.

6. Investigate any of these Internet sites:

   The Cave of Lascaux: http://www.culture.gouv.fr/culture/arcnat/lascaux/en/

   Flints and Stones: Real Life in Prehistory: http://museums.ncl.ac.uk/flint/menu.html

   Ice Mummies (Nova Online): http://www.pbs.org/wgbh/nova/icemummies/

   The Life and Times of Early Man: http://members.aol.com/Donnclass/EarlyMan.html

Unit 1 Assessment

1. Have students create an illustrated time line of the emergence of hominids and human beings.

2. Have students create a class display of cave paintings, explaining the possible social and cultural meanings of each one.

3. Worksheet 4, Elements of Stone Age Life, can also serve as an effective assessment tool.

Unit 2: The Agricultural Revolution

Worksheet 1: Animals and Crops Around the World (page 17)

Students could also create a time line indicating approximate earliest dates (and places) where these plants and animals were domesticated and tended. They could also select a single plant or animal and do an in-depth report on its domestication and its place in ancient agricultural societies.

sheep—Middle East, Southeast Asia, North Africa

goat—Middle East, North Africa, Southeast Asia

cattle—Europe, North Africa, Southeast Asia

pig—Europe, North Africa, Southeast Asia, China

guinea pig—Central/South America

water buffalo—Southeast Asia, China, India

llama—Central/South America

reindeer—Europe

turkey—North America

chicken—Southeast Asia

wheat—Middle East, China, India, North Africa (Nile Valley)

barley—Middle East, India, North Africa (Nile Valley)

millet—sub-Saharan Africa, China

lentil—Middle East

rice—sub-Saharan Africa, Southeast Asia, China

maize—Central/South America

sorghum—sub-Saharan Africa, North Africa

yam—Central/South America, sub-Saharan Africa, Southeast Asia

banana—Southeast Asia

potato—Central/South America

sunflower—North America

Worksheet 2: Agricultural Tools (page 18)

1. sickle blade—used to reap crops such as grains and cereals.

2. wooden plow—used to break up and turn over farm fields.

3. wheeled cart—early use of the wheel to help transport crops.

4. axe—used to clear fields of trees and other brushy growth.

5. hoe—used to till soil and remove weeds.

6. grindstone/mortar-pestle—used to grind grain.

7. Pottery served as containers for carrying and storing food, especially the food surpluses created by farming; they were also used for cooking and as dishes.

8. Using pottery containers, people could add soups, stews, and bread to their diets.

Worksheet 3: Farming Techniques (page 19)

You could assign just one of these techniques to individual students, or to small groups. Students would then share their findings with classmates.

1. Nile River floods: Egyptian farmers needed only temporary dikes to hold the Nile floodwaters on the land so they would soak in during the predictable once-yearly floods.

2. Tigris and Euphrates rivers: These rivers flooded unpredictably and tumultuously every spring; the floods were dangerous and destructive and couldn't be harnessed as the Nile flood was. Instead, farmers had to use river water during its low stage, through irrigation, by lifting or channeling the water via partial dams and long canals. These earthworks needed constant tending and repair.

3. Underground water supply: Underground canals called *qanats* lead groundwater from a hillside to farmlands below, allowing otherwise arid land to be farmed.

4. Drained field technique: Used in wet or swampy areas. People dug drainage canals to take away excess water (as well as cold air) and used the mud taken out of the canals to build up raised planting areas.

5. Wet-rice agriculture: Control of the water supply is crucial for wet-rice farming. Rice is seeded, or seedlings are set out, in flooded fields. The water can come from any source—irrigation canals, rainfall, river floods, etc.—and is held in by dikes, or embankments. The fields remain flooded as the rice grows. Shortly before the rice is ready for harvest, the fields are drained. After harvest, the fields are flooded again, and a new crop is started.

Worksheet 4: Why Be a Farmer? (page 20)

Each point is valid, but counter-arguments can be made. Farmers and herders did work much harder for longer periods every day than did food gatherers and hunters, perhaps 10 hours versus several hours a day (but in return they had a relatively secure and stable food supply, plus surpluses to store). Early farming people had a less varied and therefore less nutritious diet than food gatherers, on the whole (but they did have a steady supply of foods

they liked to eat). Permanent villages were in fact less healthy places to live; contagious diseases spread from human waste, polluted water, vermin, insects, and domestic animals (but houses provided more protection from the elements than crude huts or pits or rock overhangs). Settled farming people were vulnerable to climate variations such as drought or excessive heat or cold that could damage their crops (but on the other hand, they could lay up surpluses to use in bad times). The need to control agricultural territory led to more conflicts between people than among nomadic hunter-gatherers. And yes, farming people did have to work at building public structures in addition to their long days in the field.

Worksheet 5: Specializing (page 21)

Another example would be from general herding, to cattle herding, to animal-skin worker (fur, hide, feathers), to leather tanner (with a spin-off of dyestuff gatherer and processor), to saddlemaker and shoemaker, to bootmaker and sandalmaker. (From Richard Bulliet's "Themes, Conjectures, and Comparisons" in Heidi Roupp's *Teaching World History: A Resource Book*.)

Worksheet 6: The Evidence of Archaeology (page 22)

Suggested answers:

1. a hunting-gathering society
2. settled agricultural society with crop surpluses
3. nomadic hunter-gatherers who gathered a lot of their food from waters
4. a society with reverence for ancestors
5. cooperative agricultural society
6. hunter-gatherers
7. territorial village dwellers
8. a society that cared for disabled group members
9. a farming community whose religious practices included reverence for the Earth Mother, who exerted power over fertility and nature
10. farming society
11. hunter-gatherers
12. agricultural (herding) society

13. hunter-gatherers

14. settled village dwellers, at least seasonally

15. hunter-gatherer community whose religious beliefs centered on nature spirits

Worksheet 7: Climate and Lifestyle (page 23)

1. Cool, dry climate of northern China favors millet, is unsuitable for rice.

2. Warm, wet climate of southern China favors rice, is unsuitable for millet.

3. Wet, very humid climate of equatorial West Africa favors root crops, is unsuitable for wheat.

4. Plains of North America were unsuitable for corn in an era of primitive agricultural techniques; bison were plentiful and provided many necessities of life.

5. Most of Australia was too dry and hot for successful farming.

6. As the Sahara dried out, farming was no longer possible; for many years during this era, there was just enough vegetation to support herding.

7. Mideast barley was not suited to warm, humid conditions south of the Sahara; local grains, however, were well adapted.

8. Extremely cold conditions made farming a poor choice for this region; reindeer provided many necessities of life.

9. Plains of Central Asia were too arid to support farming, but were covered with grasslands that could support herding.

10. Mesoamerica had few native animals that were suitable for domestication; the warm climate was ideal for farming.

Worksheet 8: A Neolithic Village (pages 24–25)

You could have pairs or small teams of students work together to investigate their chosen village sites. You could ask students who choose to report on the village pictured on the second worksheet page to note which elements on the chart are visible in the photograph. When students have completed their charts, go over each element in class to provide a comparative overview of agricultural village life in Neolithic times. Discuss reasons for similarities and differences.

Additional Activity Suggestions

You could have the students do any of the following activities.

1. Research and report on the life of pastoral tribal people in central Asia during this time frame. Why would conflicts arise between pastoralists and agriculturalists?

2. Use images of Saharan rock art to show the climate changes in that region—from grassy savannas that supported a hunter-gatherer way of life to drier conditions that led to a pastoral way of life.

3. Draw up a day's menu for a hunter-gatherer, a farmer, and a pastoral person during this time frame.

4. Trace the spread of rice cultivation through Asia.

5. If you were a hunter-gatherer, what wild foods would you live on in the area where you now live?

6. Investigate any of these Internet sites:

   The Ancient Indus Valley:
   http://www.harappa.com/har/har0.html

   Ancient Sumerian Inventions:
   http://tlc.ousd.k12.ca.us/cv/projects/sumeria/sumeria.html

   Museum of Ancient Inventions
   (good for other units in this book as well):
   http://www.smith.edu/hsc/museum/ancient_inventions

   Mysteries of Çatalhöyük!:
   http://www.smm.org/catal/

Unit 2 Assessment

1. Have students compare the way of life of hunter-gatherers with the way of life of agricultural people. Why did so many early people take up farming as a new way of life?

2. Ask students to discuss the relationship of climate changes following the end of the last Ice Age to the rise of agricultural societies around the world.

3. Have students locate and label the sites of early agricultural communities on copies of world maps.

4. Have students use the information on their Worksheet 8 chart to write a descriptive essay of life in a Neolithic agricultural village.

Unit 3: The First Civilizations

Worksheet 1: Mapping the Early Civilized World (page 32)

We will revisit this map in Unit 4, when students will trace trade routes across the region. You could enlarge segments of the blank map (provided in the front matter for photocopying) to provide larger-scale map work for the separate civilized regions. The Egypt-Nubia map in Unit 4 could also be useful here.

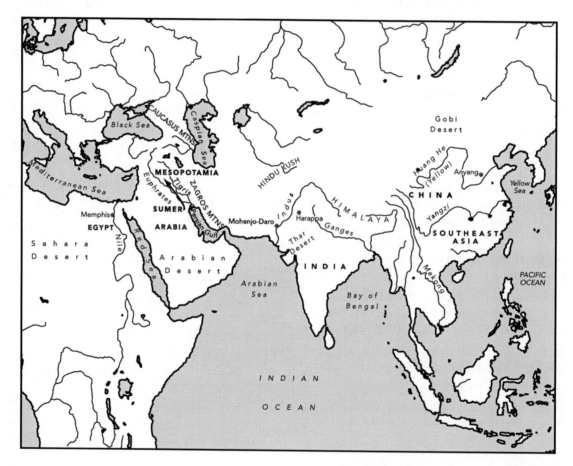

1. Barriers: mountains, deserts, large bodies of water—Egypt, India, and China

2. Many routes open to Mesopotamia; all civilizations can be entered in some fashion.

Worksheet 2: Ancient Monuments (page 33)

The model-building project could be a group activity. You could expand it by having some members of the group build the model while others create a written and/or oral report explaining the reasons and techniques for building such monuments.

1. Pyramid; Egyptian; a burial place for a pharaoh or other royal person. This could also be a Mesoamerican monument, built to raise the temple at the top toward the sun/moon.

2. Megalith; western Europe; a burial place

3. Ziggurat; Mesopotamian; built to elevate the shrine to the city's god at the top of the ziggurat (which was usually seven stories high)

4. Citadel; Indus Valley; purpose not certain—it was an elevated, enclosed compound of several large buildings, probably home to the city's central governing authority and, perhaps, central religious buildings.

Worksheet 3: Civilization and Social Classes (page 34)

This would be a good small-group activity, with students cooperatively deciding on the structure of their charts. Charts will vary, and class comparisons will provide interesting class discussions.

Generally, king/ruler will be at the top; next in line might be warriors, priests/shamans, scribes, and nobility/elite families; government officials could be in the second or third tier; then shopkeepers, merchants, local leaders/rulers, and artisans; then farmers/peasants; and last, slaves.

Worksheet 4: Building the Pyramids (pages 35–36)

Help students grasp the size of these projects by having the class identify objects, buildings, and roadways that match the various dimensions mentioned in the readings.

Worksheet 5: The Need for Technology (pages 37–38)

1. Wheel, Sumerians: needed to utilize the power of draft animals via wheeled carts, essential for large-scale agriculture.

2. Chemistry and anatomy, Egyptians: needed to create mummies, which provided a home for the departed soul; providing for the afterlife was of great importance to the ancient Egyptians.

3. Surveying and measuring, Egyptians: needed to measure the height of the Nile flood, which determined the layout of agricultural fields and dikes within the Nile flood area, and also to survey the land to redraw boundaries of fields after the annual flood.

4. Astronomy and mathematics, Mesopotamians: needed for precise observations of the movements of astronomical bodies, which allowed the Mesopotamians to foretell future events.

Astronomy and mathematics, Olmec, Egyptians, Chinese: to understand and keep track of the change of seasons, and to develop calendars, for successful agriculture

5. Architecture and engineering, Mesopotamians, Chinese, Egyptians, Olmec: to construct monumental buildings and irrigation/flood-control projects

Architecture and engineering, Indus Valley people: to construct irrigation/flood-control projects and to construct large public buildings and water/sewer systems for carefully planned cities

Answer to Challenge Question: The Phoenicians developed the first alphabet, and the Lydians issued the first coins.

Worksheet 6: Origins of Writing (page 39)

Answer to Challenge Question: Some ideas can't be easily expressed in pictures. Mastering a writing system with numerous symbols required a lot of time and schooling; only members of the elite classes had the leisure and wealth needed to learn to read and write. See the Additional Activity Suggestions for another activity involving ancient writing systems.

1. Character writing, China, for recording ritual questions and answers on oracle bones

2. Cuneiform, Sumer, to keep track of commercial transactions and facilitate government administration

3. Hieroglyphics, Egypt, to record religious rituals and information about annual Nile floods; also to facilitate complex and extensive administrative bureaucracy

Worksheet 7: The Mighty Gilgamesh (pages 40–41)

For Gilgamesh Internet sites, see "Internet Ancient History Sourcebook: Mesopotamia" at http://www.fordham.edu/halsall/ancient/asbook03.html.

1. The king is all-powerful, a mighty warrior, and is appointed and favored by the god that protects the city.

2. It expresses the transition from the wild hunting-gathering way of life to the settled, town-based agricultural way of life. Enkidu becomes civilized as he has sexual relations with a woman, eats cooked food, drinks alcoholic beverages, longs for human companionship, dons clothes, washes himself, and heads for town.

3. This expresses the people's inability to stand against their strong ruler's desires and edicts. They yield to him and embrace his protection as the strongest person in the kingdom. They admire his prowess in battle.

4. Mesopotamian gods, like Humbaba, were fearsome and dangerous, and uninterested in people's welfare.

Worksheet 8: Marks of Civilization (page 42)

You could assign this as a group activity, specifying Egyptian, Sumerian/Mesopotamian, Indus Valley, or Shang Chinese civilization for each group. You could also use this activity sheet while working on Unit 4, allowing students to choose from a much greater variety of civilizations, including Nubian, Olmec, Celtic, Korean, and so on.

When charts are completed, lead a class discussion about each element in which students contrast and compare the various aspects of the four early river floodplain civilizations.

Additional Activity Suggestions

You could have the students do any of the following activities.

1. Describe the climate variations in the different regions of India or China and the effect these variations have on people's ways of life.

2. Do some research on Chinese, ancient Egyptian, or ancient Sumerian writing systems. Then create a sign for a business or an inscription on a monument in one of these civilizations in the appropriate writing. Can any of your classmates decipher your writing?

3. Research and report on the devastating 1998 floods in the river floodplains of China. Show images of the flooding if possible. Why would China still be so vulnerable to flooding, given that it has been a problem since ancient times?

4. Compare the flood story in *The Epic of Gilgamesh* with the flood story in the Bible's Book of Genesis. What would account for the similarities between them?

5. Research and report on ancient Egyptian medical knowledge and techniques.

6. Find out why the Indus River writing system has not yet been deciphered.

7. Compare the status of women in the early river floodplain civilizations. Why is so little known about this subject?

8. Investigate any of these Internet sites:

Ancient Egypt:
http://www.ancientegypt.co.uk/menu.html

Ancient Egypt Webquest:
http://www.iwebquest.com/egypt/ancientegypt.htm

Ancient Sumerian Inventions:
http://tlc.ousd.k12.ca.us/cv/projects/sumeria/sumeria.html

Daily Life in Ancient China:
http://members.aol.com/Donnclass/Chinalife.html

Daily Life in Ancient India:
http://members.aol.com/Donnclass/Indialife.html

Evolution of Alphabets:
http://www.wam.umd.edu/~rfradkin/alphapage.html

Institute of Egyptian Art and Archaeology:
http://www.memphis.edu/egypt/

Internet Indian History Sourcebook:
http://www.fordham.edu/halsall/india/indiasbook.html

Mesopotamia:
http://www.cmi.k12.il.us/Urbana/projects/AncientCiv/Meso/meso.html

The Mummy Tombs:
http://www.mummytombs.com/

Transformation of English Letters to
Hieroglyphic:
http://www.tourism.egnet.net/Cafe/
TOR_TRN.asp

Write Like a Babylonian
(see your monogram in cuneiform):
http://www.upennmuseum.com/cgi-bin/cune-
iform.cgi

Unit 3 Assessment

1. Have students discuss the similarities and differences among the various river floodplain civilizations.

2. Ask students to explain why early Egypt united
into a kingdom under one strong ruler, with a
single military force, while early Mesopotamia
fragmented into warring and competing city-
states, each with its own army.

Unit 4: Civilizations Spread and Change

Worksheet 1: Ancient Trade Networks (page 49)

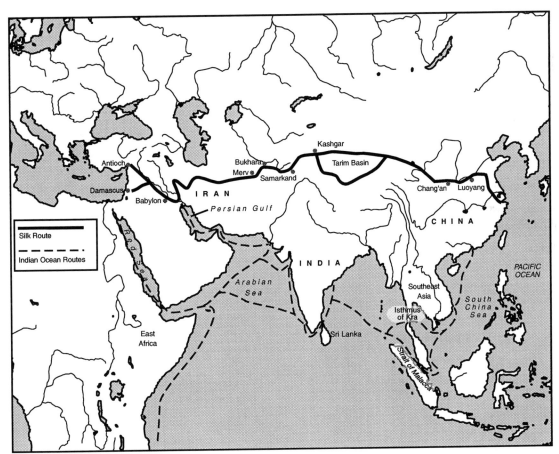

Symbols for the trade goods will vary. Check to be sure they are in roughly the correct places on
students' maps.

Worksheet 2: Your Trading Expedition (page 50)

You could tell students that an overland caravan traveled an average of 20 miles per day.

Worksheet 3: Nubia: African Crossroads (page 51)

1. It was the only continuously inhabited north–south link between Egypt/North Africa and sub-Saharan Africa. It linked tropical Africa with the Mediterranean region. It also formed an east–west link from the Red Sea into the African savanna.

2. It had rich gold deposits, plus copper and semi-precious stones. It created a profitable export trade in these goods. It was also rich in iron ore and timber. Its capital, Meroë, became an important iron-producing center.

3. Cataracts on the Nile blocked boat traffic. Travelers had to walk or ride on tracks around the cataracts.

Time line:

c. 1500 B.C.E.—Egypt takes control of Nubia.

c. 750 B.C.E.—Nubia takes control of Egypt.

c. 650 B.C.E.—Assyrians sweep into Egypt, push out Nubians.

c. 500 B.C.E.—Meroë becomes Nubian capital and a great iron-producing center.

c. 350 C.E.—Axum invades and destroys Nubia.

Worksheet 4: Women of Mesopotamia (page 52)

The differences are reflective of the "rule of reason" of Hammurabi/Babylon versus the ruthless empire of Assyria.

For the chart work, you could list civilizations for students to investigate, and you could assign this as a group activity. Ask students to search for a possible pattern in their completed charts—for example, did the status of women decline over time in Mesopotamia, as possibly indicated by the differences in the laws quoted on the activity sheet?

Worksheet 5: War Technology 1 (page 53)

1. Blades made of iron were stronger, harder, more durable, and stayed sharp longer.

2. The composite bow had extreme string tension, so arrows shot from it flew much farther than from earlier bows.

3. The Assyrians perfected siege machinery, which allowed them to conquer walled cities. Huge battering rams broke down walls, while mobile towers elevated archers above the height of defenders.

4. Speedy chariots, drawn by powerful war horses, gave riders an enormous advantage over relatively immobile foot soldiers.

5. Cavalry soldiers were much more maneuverable than chariot or foot soldiers.

6. Cataphracts had the strength and stamina to carry heavily armed and armored soldiers.

7. Stirrups made it much easier for soldiers to stay in the saddle, using their legs and feet, while using both arms to wield weapons.

Students who complete the Extra Challenge Activity will see that many of these innovations were first developed by the nomadic peoples of central Asia.

Additional Activity Suggestion #1 provides an exploration of another aspect of ancient war technology.

Worksheet 6: Moving Populations (page 54)

Sample examples:

1. Hittites, Assyrians

2. Celts in Rome

3. Hyksos in Egypt, Kassites in Babylonia, Babylonians in Sumeria

4. Aryans in India

5. nomads north of China

Worksheet 7: The Celts (page 55)

Students could use the "Marks of Civilization" activity sheet from Unit 3 to help answer the "civilized or barbarian" question.

Ask students what other examples of overwhelming battle cries have intimidated opposing armies in history. In the United States, examples would include the rebel yell of the Civil War and the battle cries of Native Americans.

Worksheet 8: Religious Beliefs (page 56)

1. Chinese
2. Celtic
3. Phoenician
4. Babylonian
5. Egyptian
6. Hebrew
7. Chinese
8. Nubian
9. Celtic
10. Sumerian
11. Egyptian

Worksheet 9: Copper, Bronze, and Iron (page 57)

1. It is relatively easy to extract copper from ore. Copper tools are more durable and less likely to crack or flake than stone tools. It is easier to hammer copper into desired shapes than to chip away at stone to try to achieve a desired shape. Also, copper can be shaped by pouring it in molten form into a mold. However, copper is too soft to hold a sharp edge or to do heavy work.

2. Shang-era artisans were renowned for their skilled and beautiful bronze works. The student "artisan" should show some images of Shang bronze artworks to the "patron." Copper and tin, which are mixed to create bronze, were not plentiful in northern China, so bronze was expensive and produced in only limited quantities. Bronze objects were owned mostly by members of the elite. (Bronze, an alloy, is stronger than copper, and thus makes stronger tools and weapons as well as art objects. In Shang China, the limited amounts of bronze available were used for upper-class weapons, rituals, and artworks. Peasants continued to use stone tools.)

3. Iron is found in more places and in greater quantities than copper or tin. Iron is stronger than either copper or bronze, so tools and weapons made from it keep a sharp edge longer and are less likely to break. Stronger weapons give an army a great advantage over its foes. However, the process of purifying iron ore and working it is complex. To be efficient, an ironworking center needs abundant supplies of both iron ore and wood to make the charcoal that fires the smelting process. Fortunately for the Hittites, their Asia Minor homeland of Anatolia was rich in both iron ore and wood.

4. As explained in number 2, Chinese peasants continued to use stone tools even after bronze was created. Knowledge of ironworking reached China about 500 B.C.E. Stronger, sharper iron tools made farming work easier to do and more productive. Iron ore was plentiful, as opposed to copper and tin. The Zhou developed a superior method of processing iron ore, using blast furnaces to produce cast iron, a technique that did not reach Europe until the Middle Ages.

Additional Activity Suggestions

You could have the students do any of the following activities.

1. Create a poster-illustration of a Phoenician warship, pointing out the various features that made it an effective fighting machine.

2. Trace the role of the horse as it developed over time in ancient societies. What were its most important uses? In which societies did it play a large part?

3. Map the movements of some or all of the following people, from their original locations to their new territories (and back again, if appropriate): Akkadians, Babylonians, Hittites, Kassites, Achaeans, Hyksos, Hebrews, Assyrians, Scythians, Chaldeans, Aryans, Dorians, Parthians, Mongolian Steppe nomads, Battle-Axe Folk, Celts.

4. Create a chart that shows the roles and duties of religious leaders such as priests and shamans in various ancient societies.

5. Research and report on the Nok ironworking society of Africa.

6. Find examples of Egyptian artwork that reflect the impact of interaction with Nubia. Similarly, find examples of Nubian art that reflect Egyptian contact and influence.

7. Create an illustrated time line of important events and developments during this period of history.

8. Successful Mediterranean trade depended on well-designed, reliable boats. Some ancient artworks depict such boats. Also, researchers have retrieved actual boat and cargo remains from the bed of the Mediterranean Sea. Use information from these sources to create an artwork—an illustration or a model—of a Mediterranean/Aegean trading vessel. Label and explain the boat's essential features.

9. Investigate any of these Internet sites:

Ancient Mesopotamia:
http://joseph_berrigan.tripod.com/ancientbabylon/

Ancient Nubia:
http://library.thinkquest.org/22845/

Mesopotamia:
http://www.cmi.k12.il.us/Urbana/projects/AncientCiv/Meso/meso.html

Minoan Crete:
http://www.uk.digiserve.com/mentor/minoan/

You Be the Judge on Hammurabi's Code:
http://www.phillipmartin.info/hammurabi/

Unit 4 Assessment

1. Have students compare the Assyrian empire of conquest with the Phoenician empire of trade and naval dominance.

2. Ask students to summarize the history of civilizations in this time frame as marked by movements and mingling of peoples.

3. Students can collect illustrations of artifacts that display major aspects of various early civilizations. They should explain the significance and meaning of each one.

4. Have students investigate the origins of iron-making and decide on the answer to this question: Were the Hittites the first inventors of ironmaking?

Unit 5: Greeks and Persians

Worksheet 1: Mapping Ancient Greece (page 64)

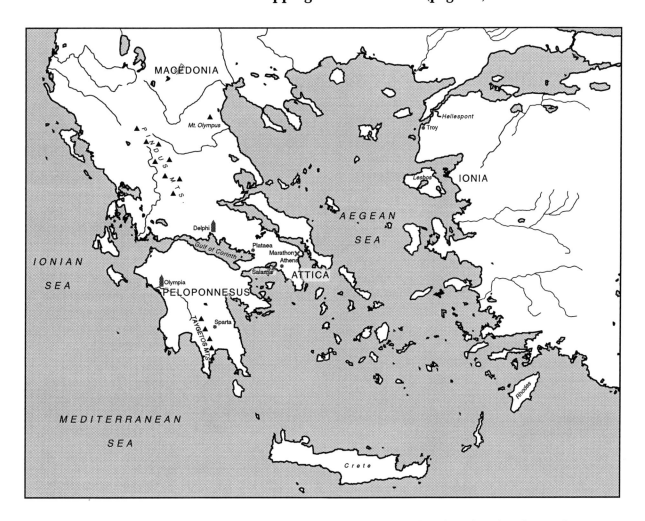

1. Mt. Olympus: home of the gods

2. Delphi: home of the oracle, who foretold the future

3. Olympia: site of the Olympic games

4. Athens: center of democracy and classic Greek culture

5. Sparta: a military society

6. Troy: site of the Trojan war

7. Lesbos: island home of the poet Sappho and her school for girls

8. Rhodes: site of a colossal sculpture that was one of the Seven Wonders of the Ancient World

9. Salamis: site of Greek defeat of Persian naval forces

10. Marathon: site of Greek defeat of Persian land forces

11. Plataea: site of decisive Greek victory over Persian forces

Worksheet 2: A Greek Science Fair (page 65)

Students' choice of activity will vary.

Worksheet 3: Greek Life in Today's Language (page 66)

1. **attic**—the space beneath the roof of a building; from Attica, whose buildings had a small upper story that rose above the main columns

2. **cynic**—a person who believes that people's actions are always based on selfish and insincere motives; from the Cynics, who believed that people should seek virtue and scorn pleasure, wealth, and social status. (The Cynics were not cynics in today's meaning of the word.)

3. **epicurean**—having sensitive and discriminating tastes, especially as relating to food and wine; from the Epicureans, who devoted themselves to the pursuit of pleasures of the senses and appetites

4. **marathon**—a footrace of 26 miles 385 yards; from Marathon, site of a Greek victory over the Persians. A runner is supposed to have run this distance to bring word of the victory to Athens, after which he collapsed and died.

5. **pyrrhic** (victory)—a victory gained at too great a cost; from Pyrrhus, king of Epirus, who won a battle in 279 B.C.E., but with such heavy losses that he is said to have declared, "One more such victory and I am lost."

6. **spartan**—marked by strict self-discipline and self-denial, extreme frugality, and avoidance of comfort; from Sparta, which developed its society along those lines

7. **stoic**—outwardly unaffected by pain or pleasure; from the Stoics, who advocated this approach to life

8. **thespian**—an actor; from Thespis, supposed to be the first man to play a role on the Greek stage

Extra Challenge word meanings and Greek history origins:

draconian—extremely severe; from Draco, a Greek who drew up a harsh code of laws

laconic—using short, abrupt speech; from Laconia, home of the militaristic Spartans, who trained their youth to speak in the fewest possible words

philippic—a speech that is a violent attack on someone; from the bitter speeches against Philip of Macedon delivered in the Assembly by Demosthenes

solon—a wise lawmaker; from Solon, who was one

sophistry—reasoning that sounds good but is basically deceptive; from the Sophists, who questioned and studied established ideas and had a reputation for tricky argumentation

sybaritic—loving luxury and sensual pleasure; from Sybaris, a Greek colony-city in Italy marked by great wealth and luxury

Worksheet 4: Greek Women (page 67)

1. A free woman of Athens had very little freedom. She spent her life cloistered in the women's quarters of her home, tending to household matters. She seldom appeared in public and did not join her husband when he entertained friends at home.

2. A free woman of Sparta had more freedom. Spartan women and girls were encouraged to engage in robust physical activity so they would be healthy and thus able to produce healthy males to serve in Sparta's army.

3. A slave woman of Athens actually had more freedom than her mistress, for she could leave the house to do the shopping and other errands. However, she was subject to the sexual demands of her master and had to obey orders from both the master and mistress.

4. A slave woman of Sparta led a dismal life as a helot, the despised, exploited, and feared class of people who had been conquered and enslaved by the Spartans.

Worksheet 5: The Plague in Athens (page 68)

As an Extra Challenge, students could research and report on other epidemics/pandemics in history—for example, the Black Death in Europe and the flu pandemic during World War I.

1. Check map answers; the plague moves from Ethiopia into Egypt and Libya, then spreads to Athens through the Persian Empire (possibly arriving by ship at Piraeus, the port city of Athens).

2. This occurred during the Peloponnesian War, when Athens needed to be strong in its battle with Sparta.

3. The city was overcrowded with people who had moved in to escape the war; the city had poor sewage disposal and crowded, twisty, and garbage-filled streets; and people had no knowledge of hygiene or sanitation.

Worksheet 6: Alexander and Hellenization (page 69)

1. To secure the good will of the people he had conquered, by treating them as equals.

2. Clothing—Alexander adopted the Persian style of dress.

Government—Alexander kept local Persian administration models, but he replaced Persian officials with Greek/Macedonian ones.

Education of young people—Persian boys were taught Greek and trained in Macedonian military skills.

Other intermarriages—Alexander encouraged as many as 10,000 Macedonian soldiers to marry native women throughout his realm, bestowing them with wedding gifts.

New cities—Alexander established Greek-style cities at strategic points in his realm and settled retired and wounded soldiers there.

Worksheet 7: Persians Versus Greeks (page 70)

The predictions were accurate. The Greeks were fighting for their homeland and were a homogeneous group. Xerxes' soldiers were far from their native lands and came from a wide variety of nations. The farther into Greece that Xerxes' armies marched, the longer their supply route became, and the farther from Xerxes' home base his ships were, and the longer they were gone, the more difficult it became to resupply them.

Worksheet 8: The First Historians (page 71)

Students' answers will vary.

Additional Activity Suggestions

You could have the students do any of the following activities.

1. Compare Persian and Greek religious beliefs.

2. On your map of the ancient world, outline Alexander's empire at its farthest extent. Then show how the empire split up after Alexander's death.

3. Write a letter home from one of Alexander's Macedonian soldiers telling about the fascinating new people and places he encounters on his travels with the army.

4. Explain the different definitions of the "good life" developed by Greek philosophers.

5. Create a diagram of one of the four major battles of the Persian War.

6. Create a model or plan of a typical Greek polis.

7. Read the portion of Herodotus' *History* (Book 8) that describes the soldiers of many different nations in Xerxes' army. Create illustrations of some or many of these soldiers, with their different and distinctive clothing styles.

8. Research the volcanic destruction of the island of Thera. Write a vivid "you are there" description of it. For writing models, see Pliny the Younger's description of the eruption of Mt. Vesuvius and contemporary accounts of the eruptions of Krakatoa and Mt. Saint Helens. Then answer these questions: (1) Do you think Thera could be the lost city of Atlantis? (2) Could the volcanic event at Thera have caused a tidal wave that parted the Red Sea for the Hebrews escaping from slavery in Egypt?

9. Create an illustrated time line of events and accomplishments during this period of history.

10. Investigate any of these Internet sites:

Alexander the Great on the Web (including "Alexander in Images"): http://www.isidore-of-seville.com/alexander/

The Ancient City of Athens: http://www.indiana.edu/~kglowack/athens/

Ancient Greece: http://www.ancientgreece.com/

The Ancient Greek World:
http://www.museum.upenn.edu/
Greek_World/Index.html

Daily Life in Ancient Greece:
http://members.aol.com/Donnclass/
Greeklife.html

Unit 5 Assessment

1. Ask students to describe Greek innovations and accomplishments in one (or more) of the following areas: government, science, architecture, sculpture, poetry, drama, philosophy, history. They should provide examples of such work when feasible. For example, for accomplishments in artistic areas, they could create displays of illustrations of outstanding Greek artworks.

2. Have students draw up a "balance sheet" showing the benefits and costs of Alexander's conquests.

Unit 6: Major Religions and Ethical Systems

Worksheet 1: The Bhagavad Gita (page 77)

Use the reading of these excerpts to have a class discussion of the concept of a rigid class and caste system—so alien to the individualistic, socially mobile society of North America. Ask students to consider the advantages of such a system—security, contentment with your place, commitment to fulfill your sphere in the best possible way, understanding of what is expected of you, stability of the society, and so on. Do you have any Hindus in your class who can more fully explain the class and caste system? (Be sure students remain respectful of the different systems and traditions of all classmates.)

Remind students that there was a fifth group of people, the Untouchables, below and outside of the class structure, who are not mentioned in the Gita. You could discuss how and why this class developed.

1. reincarnation—rebirth of the soul, the continuing cycle of death and rebirth

2. Brahmans—priests and scholars

Kshatriyas—warriors, rulers, government officials

Vaisyas—farm owners, herders, traders, merchants

Shudras—peasants, laborers

Worksheet 2: The Buddhist Path (page 78)

Answers will vary somewhat. You could have students think about the exercise and questions and then work out possible answers in class.

Worksheet 3: The Ten Commandments (page 79)

Answers will vary. The Ten Commandments speak about worship on the Sabbath, while the Eightfold Path and the Buddhist rules do not. Other elements could be related to one another.

Worksheet 4: The Christian Ideal (page 80)

Answers will vary. In general, Jesus Christ explained the Ten Commandments in a broad way to cover many areas of human conduct, not in a narrow legalistic way adhering to the exact language of the edicts.

Worksheet 5: The Wisdom of Confucius (pages 81–82)

Responses will vary. Suggest that students use simple nouns or adjectives for their list, such as *justice* or *just*, or *sincerity* or *sincere*. You could then develop a comprehensive list on the board and winnow students' suggestions to a succinct list of the most important Confucian qualities.

Worksheet 6: The Place of Women (page 83)

Answers will vary. Women had a more equal role under Buddhist than under Confucian teachings. In real life, lower-class women had to be less restricted in their activities in order to contribute needed help to the family economics—for example, by running a shop or a market stall.

For the Extra Challenge, you could use group work for the discussion, chart, or role-play. For the "day in the life" sketch, you could assign one particular culture to each group or let students choose one culture to write about, and then share the various sketches with the whole class.

Worksheet 7: Religious and Ethical Beliefs (page 84)

1. Ch, H
2. Ch, H
3. D, B, Chr
4. V, H, later Chr
5. B, Chr, Cf
6. B, V, H, J, Chr
7. B, Chr
8. J, Chr
9. V, H
10. B
11. Cf, D, Ch
12. V, H, J, Ch
13. D, B
14. V, H, J, Chr, later B
15. V, H, J, Chr, Ch
16. B, Cf
17. Cf, V, H
18. Ch

Allow for some variation in interpretation.

Additional Activity Suggestions

You could have the students do any of the following activities.

1. Read some of the parables of Jesus and the Buddhist Jakata tales, and draw comparisons between them.

2. Compare events in Hebrew history as related in the Bible with known historical events in the Middle East. Create a time line of these events. Trace the wanderings of the Hebrews through the Middle East region on a map.

3. Read the *Upanishads* to learn more about Buddhist teachings. Similarly, read more Christian and Jewish sacred texts and Confucian analects to learn more about those religious/ethical belief systems.

4. Locate and trace on a map the areas where each of these major religions/ethical belief systems developed and flourished during this time period.

5. Most of the cultures that this unit focuses on were patriarchal and patrilineal—for example, societies dominated by Confucian, Judaic, Hindu, and Christian beliefs. Yet in ancient times, many societies had been matriarchal or matrilineal—for example, many hunter-gatherer societies, and Nubia—and/or had worshipped female deities or an Earth Mother. What factors contributed to this gradual shift in women's roles and status in most societies over time?

6. Investigate any of these Internet sites:

   Daily Life in Ancient China:
   http://members.aol.com/Donnclass/Chinalife.html

   Daily Life in Ancient India:
   http://members.aol.com/Donnclass/Indialife.html

   Internet Indian History Sourcebook:
   http://www.fordham.edu/halsall/india/indiasbook.html

   For the teacher:

   Brief History of Buddhism:
   http://mcel.pacificu.edu/as/students/vb/History.HTM

   Hinduism for Schools:
   http://www.btinternet.com/~vivekananda/schools1.htm

   Judaism and Jewish Resources:
   http://shamash.org/trb/judaism.html

Unit 6 Assessment

1. Have students explain how Buddhism developed in reaction to Hinduism. (Extension: Also explain how Daoism developed in reaction to Confucianism.)

2. Have students compare the reasons and methods used to spread these major religions out from the core region where each developed.

3. Students can create a class display of religious art that expresses important basic beliefs of these major religions. They should explain what each artwork expresses.

Unit 7: Great Empires

Have students look at their map of the ancient world as they read the student background information about Rome. Point out the central location of Rome on the Italian peninsula and the central location of the Italian peninsula within the Mediterranean region.

Worksheet 1: Slavery in the Ancient World (page 91)

Answers will vary.

Worksheet 2: War Technology 2 (page 92)

1. Trireme—Greek origin; was swift and maneuverable, had a ram to disable and/or sink enemy vessels, had rowers as well as sails, so was not dependent on wind

2. Phalanx—Greek origin, improved by Macedonians; heavily armored infantry soldiers fought in a closely packed formation with long spears; the enemy could not penetrate the solid line of armor before the long spears decimated them.

3. Catapult—Macedonian origin; an advance in siege equipment, it used twisted cords to hurl stones or arrows great distances against fortified enemy positions.

4. Crossbow—Chinese origin; propelled arrows with tremendous force and swiftness—arrows could pierce armor.

Worksheet 3: Mapping the Chinese Empire (page 93)

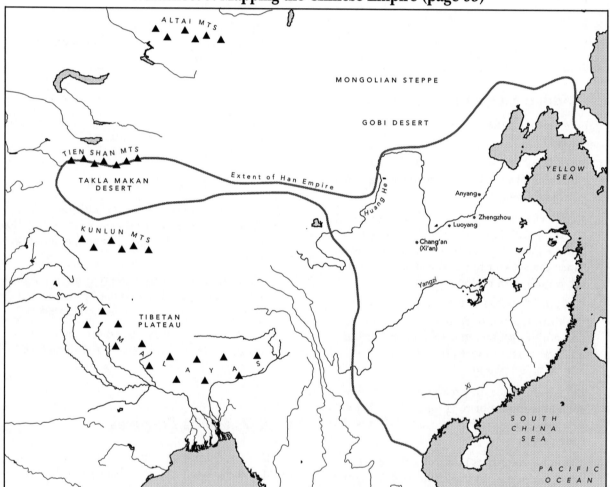

After students complete their maps, ask them to answer these Challenge Questions.

1. What natural barriers isolated China from other civilizations? [On the west, the Takla Makan Desert and the Tibetan Plateau, as well as the Tien Shan and Kunlun mountains. To the southwest, the formidable Himalaya Moun-

tains. To the north, the desolate Gobi Desert and the Mongolian Steppe, and also the Altai mountains. To the east, the Pacific Ocean.]

2. What region(s) of China was (were) suitable for farming? [The river plains between the Huang He and Yangzi rivers.]

Worksheet 4: The Life of Chinese Peasants (page 94)

Students' choice of activities will vary.

Worksheet 5: The Mandate of Heaven (page 95)

As an Extra Challenge, you could ask students what other ancient (or more modern) societies considered that their rulers had divine status or a divine mandate—for example, the Mesopotamians and the Egyptians.

1. Students' answers will vary. Basically, the Mandate gave emperors divine authority to rule, so long as they ruled well. Should they become nonvirtuous rulers, they would lose the Mandate and be eligible to be overthrown by others whom the gods would then favor.

2. The Zhou overthrew the Shang, and the Mandate of Heaven gave them a justification for having done this, claiming that the Shang had become corrupt and had lost their mandate.

Worksheet 6: Mapping the Indian Empire (page 96)

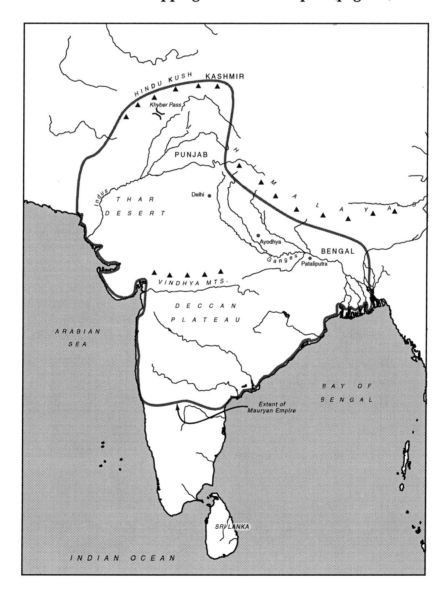

After students complete their maps, ask them to answer these Challenge Questions.

1. What features of Indian geography encouraged the development of many different societies and ways of life? [The many different geographical regions helped produce many different ways of life adapted to the various conditions. The mountains to the north were a partial barrier to invasions or in-migrations, but the Khyber Pass did allow new people to come in to India.]

2. Which countries of today were part of the Mauryan Empire? [Pakistan, Nepal, Bhutan, Bangladesh, India]

Worksheet 7: Women in India (page 97)

You could have students answer the questions in a number of ways: class discussion, small-group work to make the comparisons, individual essays. Students could refer to the Unit 6 worksheet, "The Place of Women."

Worksheet 8: Women Rule in Egypt (page 98)

You could assign some students to research Hatshepshut and others to research Cleopatra, with an emphasis on how each ruler acquired and used power. Students could then compare and contrast their findings in class.

Worksheet 9: Greek and Roman Architecture: A Local Hunt (page 99)

You could ask students to find on the Internet and print out images of ancient Greek and Roman public buildings. Students could then create a class display of these images and use them in their local architectural hunt.

Worksheet 10: An Empire Falls (page 100)

Students could also find and read other accounts by ancient writers of battles of their times. This could inspire their own first-person accounts of the battles. Or they could create diagrams of the battles as they developed.

You could also use this reading as a springboard to discuss reasons for the decline and fall of the Roman Empire, and then to compare those reasons

with the reasons that the empires of Alexander the Great, Mauryan India, and Han China ended.

Worksheet 11: The Empires of Rome and Han China (pages 101–102)

You could make this a small-group activity. After students complete their charts, go over the results, which may vary somewhat and will yield a master chart you and the class could fill in as a wrap-up to this unit. You could also discuss with students the reasons for the similarities and differences between the two empires. As an extension, you could add Mauryan India to the comparison activity.

Additional Activity Suggestions

You could have the students do any of the following activities.

1. Read some of the edicts of Ashoka, the great emperor of India, that Ashoka had carved on rock pillars after his conversion to Buddhism. One source of these edicts is the Internet site http://www.cs.colostate.edu/~malaiya/ashoka.html titled "The Edicts of King Ashoka."

2. Describe Chinese inventions and technological improvements during this time frame.

3. Create a series of maps or map overlays to compare these empires: Roman, Han, Mauryan, Alexander (Macedonian/Persian), Persian, Assyrian.

4. Explain why the early Italians did not base their growing civilization on sea trading as the Greeks had done.

5. Develop short biographies of the outstanding figures in the Roman, Han Chinese, and Mauryan Indian empires.

6. Read historical fiction set in these empires and then write a series of journal entries about your life as a common person in one of them.

7. Investigate any of these Internet sites:

   Daily Life in Ancient China:
   http://members.aol.com/Donnclass/Chinalife.html

   Daily Life in Ancient India:
   http://members.aol.com/Donnclass/Indialife.html

Daily Life in Ancient Rome:
http://members.aol.com/Donnclass/
Romelife.html

Dead Romans:
http://home.nyc.rr.com/deadromans/

Forum Romanum:
http://www.geocities.com/Athens/Forum/
6946/rome.html

Internet Indian History Sourcebook:
http://www.fordham.edu/halsall/india/
indiasbook.html

The Romans:
http://www.bbc.co.uk/education/romans/
home.html

Unit 7 Assessment

1. The worksheet "The Empires of Rome and Han China" can serve as an effective assessment vehicle.

2. On their maps of the ancient world, have students show the extent of Alexander's empire and the extent of the Roman Empire. Which was larger? Which lasted longer? What was the legacy of each? Why?

3. Tell students the following: "You have an urgent message to deliver from Rome to the most remote eastern region of the Roman Empire. Trace your route, and tell what various forms of transportation you will use and how long it will take to get your message to its destination."

4. Have students compare the military leadership of various famous generals in ancient history, such as Alexander the Great, Philip of Macedon, Hannibal, Ashoka, and Julius Caesar. What qualities do they have in common?

ADDITIONAL RESOURCES

Classical Literature

Aeniad, Virgil

Analects, Confucius

Arthashastra, Kautilya

Bhagavad Gita

The Bible

Book of History (Shu Ching)

Book of Songs (Zhou China)

Book of the Dead (ancient Egypt)

Chinese history: Ban family and Sima Qian

City of God, St. Augustine

The Epic of Gilgamesh

Greek comedy: Aristophanes

Greek drama: Aeschylus, Sophocles, and Euripides

Greek history: Herodotus and Thucydides

I Ching (or *Yi Jing, The Book of Changes*)

The Iliad and *The Odyssey,* Homer

Mahabharata

The Metamorphoses (and other poetry), Ovid

Ramayana

The Republic, Plato

Roman history: Livy and Tacitus

The Torah

Tripitaka (the Buddha's teachings)

Upanishads

Vedas

The Way of Virtue (Dao De Ching), Laozi

Collections of Primary Source Documents: Print

Andrea, Alfred J., and James H. Overfield. *The Human Record: Sources of Global History (Vol. 1).* Boston: Houghton Mifflin, 2001.

Frazee, Charles, ed. *World History: Original and Secondary Source Readings (Vol. 1).* San Diego: Greenhaven Press, 1999.

Hughes, Sarah Shaver and Brady Hughes. *Women in World History (Vol. 1).* Armonk, NY: M.E. Sharpe, 1995.

Kishlansky, Mark A., ed. *Sources of World History: Readings for World Civilization (Vol. 1).* New York: HarperCollins College Publishers, 1995.

Lattimore, Owen and Eleanor Lattimore, eds. *Silks, Spices and Empire.* New York: Delacorte Press, 1968.

Reilly, Kevin, ed. *Worlds of History: A Comparative Reader (Vol. 1).* Boston: Bedford/St. Martins Press, 2000.

Riley, Philip F., et al., eds. *The Global Experience: Readings in World History to 1500 (Vol. 1).* Englewood Cliffs, NJ: Prentice Hall, 1987.

Stearns, Peter N., ed. *World History in Documents: A Comparative Reader.* New York: New York University Press, 1998.

Wiesner, Merry E., et al., eds. *Discovering the Global Past: A Look at the Evidence (Vol. I),* 2d ed. Boston: Houghton Mifflin, 2002.

CD-ROM

Ancient Civilizations (Entrex)

Ancient Empires: Decisions, Decisions, Decisions (Tom Snyder Productions)

Ancient Origins (Maris)

Carmen Sandiego's Great Chase Through Time (Broderbund)

Chronicle Encyclopedia of History (Dorling Kindersley)

Egypt: Voyage to the Land of the Pharaohs (Montparnasse)

Encarta Africana (Microsoft)

Exploring Ancient Cities (Teotihuacan, Pompeii, Petra, and Crete) (Sumeria)

The First Emperor of China (Voyager)

Geosafari History (Educational Insights)

Historical Images on CD-ROM: World History (Instructional Resources Corp.)

History Through Art Series: Ancient Greece; Ancient Rome (Clearvue)

Nile: Passage to Egypt (Discovery Channel)

Religions of the World (Clearvue, Mentorom)

The Road to Ancient Egypt; The Road to Ancient Greece; The Road to Ancient Rome (Thomas S. Klise)

The Silk Road (DNA Multimedia)

Starsites: Ancient Buildings Connecting Earth and Sky (DNA Multimedia)

The Story of Civilization by Will and Ariel Durant (World Library)

Timeliner (Tom Snyder Productions)

Time Traveler CD: A Multimedia Chronicle of History (New Media Schoolhouse)

Up to the Himalayas: Kingdoms in the Clouds (DNA Multimedia)

Video

Africa: A Voyage of Discovery with Basil Davidson (1: Different But Equal and Mastering a Continent) (RM Arts)

Alexander the Great: Conquerors (Discovery Channel School)

Ancient Civilizations (recreations of ruins) (Questar)

Buddhism: The Middle Way of Compassion (United Learning)

The David Macaulay Series (Pyramid, Roman City) (PBS Home Video)

Discovering Ancient Greece (United Learning)

Egypt: Quest for Eternity (National Geographic)

Faith and Belief: Five Major World Religions (Knowledge Unlimited)

The Great Wall: In Search of History (History Channel)

The Greeks: In Search of Meaning (Learning Corp. of America)

Hinduism: An Ancient Path in the Modern World (United Learning)

History Through Literature Series (Clearvue/eav) includes:
  Civilization and Writing: 10,000–55 B.C.
  Empires of Heaven and Earth: The World in Roman Times, 300 B.C.–A.D. 476
  Philosophy and Government: The World in Greek Times, 800–287 B.C.

Judaism: The Religion of a People (United Learning)

Life in Ancient Rome (Encyclopedia Britannica)

Lost Civilizations (Time-Life)

Mysteries of Egypt (National Geographic)

Pyramids: Majesty and Mystery (History Channel)

Religions of the World Series (Schlessinger)

The Romans: Life, Laughter, and Law (Learning Corp. of America)

Rome: Power and Glory (Questar)

Secrets of Lost Empires Series (WGBH/BBC)

Spartacus (starring Kirk Douglas) (Universal)

The Story of Islam: Faith and Nations (United Learning)

The World: A Television History Series (numerous titles, Network Television Production)

The World of Ancient Rome (United Learning)

World Wide Web/Internet

Sites with numerous links to world history sources are listed below. Sites of more specific interest are listed where appropriate in the Answers and Additional Activities section above. Be aware that URLs do change and sites vanish. If an URL listed here yields no results, try searching with the site title given below.

The Avalon Project at Yale Law School (a large collection of historical documents): http://www.yale.edu/lawweb/avalon/avalon.htm

History/Social Studies for K–12 Teachers (includes site map, What's New Archive, sources arranged by category): http://my.execpc.com/~dboals/boals.html

History Central Catalogue (University of Kansas site with links to every imaginable aspect of history): http://www.ukans.edu/history/VL/

Internet History Sourcebooks Project (amazing site for primary sources in many specific areas of history/geography): http://www.fordham.edu/halsall/

Kathy Schrock's Guide for Educators—World and Ancient History Sites (a Cape Cod teacher's excellent list of resources): http://school.discovery.com/schrockguide/history/histw.html

GLOSSARY

agricultural revolution—the widespread change from the hunting-gathering way of life to the farming ways of life

aristocracy—government by a small, privileged upper class

B.C.E.—"Before the Common Era," equivalent to B.C. ("Before Christ")

C.E.—"Common Era," equivalent to A.D. (*anno Domini*, "in the year of the Lord")

caste—Hindu birth group

city-state—a city and the surrounding village and farmlands it controlled

civilization—highly developed, complex form of human culture

cuneiform—wedge-shaped form of writing, invented in Sumer

deity—god or goddess

democracy—government by the people, especially by the majority

domesticate—to adapt a plant or animal to life with, and to the advantage of, people

dynasty—a series of rulers from the same set of families

empire—a collection of nations and peoples ruled over by a single, powerful ruler and central government

ethical belief system—a body of beliefs that govern human conduct

ethnic—relating to races or large groups of people tied together by common culture and traits

Hellenistic—referring to Greek culture

hieroglyphics—symbol-based writing

hominid—a member of the group of creatures that walk upright, including human beings and related species

Ice Age—period when much of the world was covered with enormous ice fields

irrigation—process of bringing water to crops by artificial, rather than natural, means

migrate—to move from one place to another; **migration** is the act of migrating

monotheism—belief in one deity

Neolithic—referring to the New Stone Age; see **agricultural revolution**

nomadic—roaming from place to place, usually seasonally, to secure a group's food supply

papyrus—reeds used by ancient Egyptians to make writing materials

pastoralists—people whose way of life revolves around their large herds of animals

plague—deadly contagious disease

polytheistic—believing in multiple deities

reincarnation—belief that after death a person's immortal essence (soul) is reborn in another living body

specialization—the process by which people start concentrating on one particular way of making a living (also called **division of labor**)

species—a biological classification of related types of organisms

Stone Age—the first known period of prehistoric human culture, characterized by the use of stone tools

Focus on World History:
The Era of Early Civilizations and Empires

Share Your Bright Ideas

We want to hear from you!

Your name_____Date_____

School name_____

School address_____

City _____State _____Zip_____Phone number (_____)_____

Grade level(s) taught_____Subject area(s) taught_____

Where did you purchase this publication?_____

In what month do you purchase a majority of your supplements?_____

What moneys were used to purchase this product?

_____School supplemental budget   _____Federal/state funding   _____Personal

Please "grade" this Walch publication in the following areas:

Quality of service you received when purchasing	A	B	C	D
Ease of use	A	B	C	D
Quality of content	A	B	C	D
Page layout	A	B	C	D
Organization of material	A	B	C	D
Suitability for grade level	A	B	C	D
Instructional value	A	B	C	D

COMMENTS:_____

_____

What specific supplemental materials would help you meet your current—or future—instructional needs?

_____

Have you used other Walch publications? If so, which ones?_____

May we use your comments in upcoming communications?   _____Yes   _____No

Please **FAX** this completed form to **888-991-5755**, or mail it to

Customer Service, Walch Publishing, P. O. Box 658, Portland, ME 04104-0658

We will send you a **FREE GIFT** in appreciation of your feedback. **THANK YOU!**